THE DIGITAL
DIFFERENTIAL ANALYSER

Edited by
T. R. H. Sizer, C. Eng., M.I.E.E.

D0170950

CHAPMAN AND HALL LTD
11 NEW FETTER LANE · LONDON EC4

First published 1968
© *Terence R. H. Sizer* 1968
Printed in The Netherlands by
Nederlandse Boekdruk Industrie N.V.

Distribution in the U.S.A.
by Barnes & Noble, Inc.

CONTRIBUTORS
P. L. Owen, B.A.
D. W. Partridge, B. Sc. (Eng.)
E. Wagner, B. Sc.
J. F. Bussell, Ph.D.
G. C. Rowley, C. Eng., M.I.E.E.
K. S. White, B. Sc.
T. R. H. Sizer, C. Eng., M.I.E.E.

edited by
T. R. H. Sizer

The authors gratefully acknowledge the permission of the Comptroller H.M.S.O. to reproduce some of the material in Chapters 2, 4 and the Appendices.

Foreword

When the digital differential analyser (d.d.a.) first appeared some fifteen years ago it seemed to offer considerable possibilities for real time operation in combining the computing speed of the analogue machine with the accuracy and flexibility of the digital machine. At one time the d.d.a., operating with a small general purpose (g.p.) computer to set initial conditions and perform logical functions (as described in one chapter of this book), represented the most advanced form of computer in the navigation field. Large increases in the computing speed of the g.p. machine and a considerable reduction in size, however, led to the relegation of the d.d.a., and many would claim will soon do likewise to the analogue machine.

The large g.p. machine, because of the very flexibility that makes it so attractive, is not without its problems in the large number of instructions that are required for operation and the large, expensive store that is required for compilers to translate the user's language into machine code.

Viewed against this programming complexity, many d.d.a. operations have an attractive simplicity. For example two d.d.a. integrators connected in a sin-cosine loop, given four instructions, the scaling and initial conditions for each integrator, will produce the coordinates of points on a circle; if the output were connected to a plotter of a digitally controlled machine tool, the pen or tool would describe a circle to an accuracy determined by the increment size. In contrast, a g.p. machine would have to calculate by quite an involved process, the coordinates of each point individually, numerous instructions being required for each point.

True, the d.d.a. requires 'hardware' to replace the 'software' of the g.p. machine. But in view of modern advances in integrated circuits, there are many applications where lower total cost (capital and programming) may rest with the d.d.a. rather than with the g.p. computer.

The d.d.a. also merits consideration in comparison with the hybrid digital-analogue computer in which operational amplifiers and other analogue devices are coupled with digital logical elements and a g.p. computer.

The accuracy of d.d.a. computation is independent of the stability of electronic components, and an expensive and accuracy limiting analogue-digital interface is avoided. As voltage levels are not critical, the d.d.a. offers the possibility of replacing the cumbersome patch board of some types of analogue computer with electronic switches and stored program instructions.

A re-examination of the potentialities of the d.d.a. is thus highly opportune. This book fills a gap in computer literature and brings together much material that is not available elsewhere.

The Editor and one of the authors were responsible for the design of the first digital differential analyser to be marketed commercially in the U.K.; all contributors are writing from direct and extensive experience and have played a major part in the advancement of d.d.a. techniques. They have produced a comprehensive survey of the principles, theory and application of the d.d.a. The error and stability analysis is a particularly valuable contribution. It presents, without assumption of prior knowledge of the mathematical techniques used, two different but complementary ways of analysis; much of the material is new and not published elsewhere. Examples are given of application to a variety of problems varying from simulation to machine tool control.

Having been closely associated with the inception of much of the work described it is a particular pleasure to contribute this foreword.

Cranfield, Bedfordshire, U.K.   ANDREW STRATTON
March 1967

Contents

Contents

I: The Digital Differential Analyser

1.1 A brief history of computers

Computers fall into two categories, digital and analogue. Operations in the latter are generally regarded as corresponding to the behaviour of nature itself in that all the variables in the system are continuous functions of time, whereas in the former operations are carried out on quantized variables the values of which change only at specific instants in time.

Analogue computers reached the stage of commercial exploitation with the advent of the slide rule in 1630; their subsequent history [1] has been one of continuous although slow development. The principles of the digital computer proper, as distinct from the early calculating machines which were analogue devices, were established by Babbage between 1823 and 1833 when he proposed a mechanical Analytical Engine. The engine was never completed because, according to Wilkes [2], Babbage had differences of opinion with the only member of his staff capable of producing the accurate mechanical components so it is likely that he was also the first person in computing to meet the problem of the 'specialist'. Over a hundred years had to pass before the practical realization on a wide scale was possible of Babbage's 'store' for holding results, his 'mill' for performing logic and his decision elements. His concept of punched card input was, of course, developed later by Dr. Hollerith and, by coincidence, was available in a reliable form for digital computers when they eventually arrived.

To dwell on Babbage, he was inspired by more than the desire to build a commercial data handling machine and probably never saw the device in this light for he spoke only of the construction of a universal machine capable of dealing with a wide variety of problems. Such altruistic aims are seldom supported by funds unless there is evidence of a commercial future. In the period 1820–1830 there was no commercial necessity apparent for the machine he was proposing and he was persistently plagued by shortage of money. It is interesting to speculate whether Babbage and his machine would have made any significant impact on the subsequent development of technology had a successful version been produced.

In the latter half of the nineteenth century with the rapid expanse of industry and commerce there was appearing the necessity for the mechanized handling of commercial data. Consequently over the next fifty or so years names such as Hollerith, Powers Samas, Burroughs and Remington Rand became known through specialization in this field of activity. Later still, International Business Machines was formed and had emerged into a prominent position by the 1930's.

In 1937 Professor Aiken of Harvard in collaboration with I.B.M. began the design of an automatic, sequence-controlled calculator [2] in effect an electro-mechanical analogue of Babbage's Analytical Engine based on relay techniques. This was completed in 1944 and the era of the general purpose whole number digital computer had begun.

The history of analogue computing [1], as was said earlier, began with the invention by Oughtred in 1630 of the slide rule where scale length is the physical analogue of numbers to a logarithmic base. The device was developed by Everard about 1700 and by Mannheim in 1850. Somewhat earlier the planimeter, a form of mechanical integrator, appeared and by 1880 some 12,000 of a type known as the Amsler planimeter had been produced.

Professor J. Thomson described in 1876 [3] an improved type of mechanical integrator consisting of a disc-sphere-cylinder assembly also for use in planimeters. In 1878 Professor Sir W. Thomson (later Lord Kelvin) described the use of this integrator as the basis for an harmonic analyser [4] capable of solving differential equations by means of a closed loop system. As in the case of Babbage, the ideas were ahead of the general level of technology; for a meaningful solution integrators demanded too high an accuracy and could not have developed the gain necessary to drive coupling shafts and gear trains.

In 1931 Dr. Vannevar Bush described and built a machine [5] for the solution of differential equations up to the sixth order. This was based on an assembly of mechanical wheel and disc integrators and mechanical torque amplifiers. Integrating units could carry considerable loads allowing interconnection and back-coupling. The whole installation was physically large and at first glance resembled a small machine shop with banks of lathes and marking tables. These were, in fact, the integrators and input/output devices respectively.

A great deal of mathematical work was done on the machine both by Bush and other people. Of particular relevance is the work of Amble [6] who developed integrator schematics for servo loops and function generators.

His ideas form the basis of several of the integrator flow diagrams in Chapters 3 and 6 of this book. Accuracies of the order of 0·1 per cent are mentioned by Bush although he was careful to point out that this was a computing accuracy frequently degraded by the output devices, a problem still in evidence.

During the period 1935–1939 work on mechanical differential analysers in the United Kingdom was done mainly at Manchester and Cambridge. Two machines were produced each of eight integrators. A review of machines of that era and applications of this type of mechanical differential analyser has been made by Crank [7].

Generally analogue computers fall into two categories, differential analysers and simulators. The former solves a particular equation or set of equations within a range of coefficients whilst the latter provides a detailed working model of a physical system so that its behaviour can be examined under a wide range of conditions. Gilbert [8] deals with the difference between the two at some length.

The impetus given to analogue simulators during the period 1942–1946 arose from the need for accurate components in radar tracking equipment, gun-laying systems and navigation equipment. These requirements ensured the development and manufacture of a new class of electronic and electro-mechanical devices with a higher order of reliability than before and which where used extensively in the early post-war versions of both digital and analogue computers.

Some work has been done [10] on hybrid computers where analogue devices, such as operational amplifiers, are coupled with digital logical elements. A most interesting form of computer results which, whilst benefitting in one way from digital flexibility has the independent variable as time in the basic analogue element.

This provides a convenient point for introducing the digital differential analyser for in this machine the independent variable need not be time and for certain applications it combines the advantages of both analogue and digital computers without some of the respective disadvantages.

This book is concerned with both theoretical and practical illustrations of these applications which, typically, consist of systems with frequencies of the order of seconds/cycle.

Before proceeding with a detailed description of the d.d.a. it is necessary to examine once more, but briefly, the analogue, and digital computer.

1.2 Digital and analogue computers

The digital computer is supplied with input data in the form of numbers which represent the values of input variables measured at discrete moments in time, it is programmed by numbers, operates on numbers internally and eventually produces output numbers again at discrete moments in time. An analogue computer continuously measures physical variables such as voltage and current and is programmed, for example, by means of a pach panel engraved in symbols, to be an analogue of some physical system or of mathematical equations defining a system. Outputs are instantaneous and continuous.

Against the inherent accuracy and flexibility of the digital computer must be set the fact that it is impossible for it to produce a continuous output which most real-time systems demand for ideal operation. The analogue computer, whilst capable of producing outputs of a continuous nature, has several disadvantages probably the most serious of which for many applications is the fact that the independent variable must always be time, although in the more advanced forms there are complex computing units which can introduce programmed discontinuities and other non-linear functions.

Compared with general purpose digital computers where accuracy is a function of number length, analogue computing accuracy is less, being both a function of the number of operational amplifiers in use at given time (being directly proportional to the square root of the number of amplifiers) and inherently a function of component accuracy and stability. It is also operationally dependent on the regular calibration of current and voltage sources. The flexibility, too, of the analogue computer is relatively less because computing arrangements can only be changed by the physical rearrangement of computing elements of 'hardware'.

About 1950, design studies both in the U.S.A. and U.K. in the field of missile and aircraft control and navigation were focussing attention on these problems. The same studies were showing that there was no immediate solution possible in the application of the then contemporary general purpose (whole number) digital computer which was in general too big, consumed too much power and had a maximum solution rate which rendered inaccurate interpolation between successive output data.

Out of the considerations just described arose the concept of the d.d.a. and within a few years a whole range of machines was available [11–17].

1.3 The digital differential analyser (d.d.a.)

A d.d.a. consists of a set of integrators each of which is an analogue of the elements in the Bush mechanical differential analyser [18] mechanized by a digital process; the definition owes something to the two computing techniques already described and the field of simulation.

The d.d.a. integrator is an incremental device with its principle of operation based on the hypothesis that physical systems change only by a small amount in a small interval of time. If the increment δX is always small then:

$$\Sigma Y \delta X$$

is a close approximation to:

$$\int Y \delta X .$$

Each integrator is, in effect, a digital computer with a simple form of program and is formed by two registers of equal length designated Y and R and associated logic. The principle is described fully in Chapter 2 but it is necessary to anticipate the contents on one point of detail concerning the output ΔZ. A d.d.a. is arranged so that the output ΔZ of any one integrator may be used as the incremental input, either ΔX or ΔY, of any other thus:

if
$$Y^* = Y + \Sigma \Delta Y$$

then
$$\Delta Z = \frac{1}{r^n} Y^* \Delta X$$

or
$$Z = \frac{1}{r^n} \int Y \, dX$$

where n is the number of bits in the Y register and r is the radix of the numbers on which the d.d.a. operates. A programmer has the facility of routing the ΔZ output pulses to appropriate ΔX or ΔY inputs, a technique described fully in Chapter 3.

Machines comprising numbers of integrators can take one of two main forms, the simultaneous and the sequential. In the former all the integrators are processed simultaneously and the time taken to do this is known as the iteration period. Such an arrangement is flexible as integrators may be added at will to a given configuration without altering the iteration period. As such there is a close correspondence with mechanical (or other) differential analysers. Interconnection between the integrators is done by some physical means which route the ΔZ outputs appearing at the end of each iteration period. There is, of course, a separate arithmetic unit with each integrator.

The sequential d.d.a. is more akin to the conventional g.p. computer and the iteration period the time taken to process all the integrators in turn and in a fixed sequence. The time taken to process one integrator is called an integration period. There is only one arithmetic unit so the component situation is less complex than in the case of the simultaneous machine. Interconnection of integrators requires an intermediate store for the ΔZ outputs which are sampled at appropriate times of the iteration period. The device which performs this operation can correspond externally to the programming panel of an analogue computer but internally the mechanization is equivalent to that of the address unit of a g.p. computer. The addition of extra integrators to a sequential d.d.a. is not easily carried out and is generally avoided.

The simultaneous d.d.a. is faster in solution rate, for a given arithmetic speed, than the sequential d.d.a.. Whereas a typical iteration rate for a sequential machine is 250 per second, simultaneous machines have been designed with iteration rates of 100,000 per second. Assuming an accuracy of 0·1 per cent then this corresponds to a frequency bandwidth of 17 c/s. Although this is slower than the response of an analogue differential analyser, the stability of the solution to a set of equations and the repeatability of the results mean that the problem can be run at a speed to suit the computer without loss of accuracy.

Both versions of the d.d.a. produce only incremental changes of one quantum from the previous state but because of the principle of operation the frequency of the output can be so fast that in most applications this disadvantage is of theoretical interest only.

For control system applications the d.d.a. is a powerful tool. Analogue devices in general tend to carry more information than is necessary for the system characteristics, thus incremental computing techniques are compatible with a sampled-data form of computation [19, 20, 21]. So long as the techniques are confined to situations where system behaviour between sampling points is either known or may be disregarded, then they can be more economic than other methods.

There is one further point to be made concerning the output of the integrator, ΔZ, it must be of a form capable of being used as ΔX or ΔY inputs to integrators for, as is shown in Chapter 3, in this way the d.d.a. is programmed. Depending on the design of machine, ΔZ may be binary, that is have only the two values 'plus one increment' and 'minus one increment' in which case zero is represented by alternate plus ones and minus ones; alternatively ΔZ may be ternary with three possible values plus one, minus one and zero (or no change).

In the latter case it is possible to design the arithmetic unit [22] of the computer so that each integrator possesses a 'stall' facility; an integrator then has the added facility that it may be set to a given quiescent state other than zero and on the receipt of a 'trigger' will run back to zero emitting a pre-determined number of positive or negative ΔZ overflows. Chapters 3 and 6 introduce the facility in context.

1.4 The organization of the book
Chapter 2, written by P. L. Owen, is an introduction to the concept of digital representation of a variable leading to the case for incremental techniques which he describes in detail. He shows as an example that, assuming comparable arithmetic speeds, multiplication of two 13 bit binary numbers in a d.d.a. is 6·5 times faster than in a typical g.p. and that for computation of a trigonometric function the speed gain is of the order of 93 in the d.d.a.'s favour. He also deals with the binary rate multiplier, a device which can be compared with the d.d.a. integrator. Owen shows, however, that in general its computing rate and error magnitude are inferior. The binary rate multiplier has been used in machine-tool control applications and is described by Drew [23] in detail.

In Chapter 3, E. Wagner and D. W. Partridge develop the principles of flow charting and scaling. These are derived from first principles and standard schematics are described which are equivalent to the subroutine library of the g.p. computer. They show how, in the roles of function generation and rate control, the d.d.a. integrator is more flexible than the electronic integrator used in analogue computers.

D.d.a.'s are not without sources of error but these are different from those in analogue computers and may be quantified explicitly. The basic error source lies in the fact that representation of the variable is digital and therefore can never be exact; the operation is discrete both in time and amplitude. In Chapter 4, P. L. Owen discusses the sources of error using an analytic method and shows that the two main components are 'round off' and 'truncation'. The treatment is detailed and one conclusion is that the operation of an integrator could be improved by the introduction of a second-order into the integration process.

Reference has already been made to the role of the d.d.a. in sampled data applications. Chapter 5 is a detailed treatment of the subject by J. F. Bussell. Where P. L. Owen dealt in terms of the theory of finite difference equations, the treatment is now in terms of Z transform equations.

Chapter 6, by D. W. Partridge, is the application of a ternary d.d.a. with stall facility to the problems of aircraft stability and control. These are treated as an exercise in simulation in which the computer deals with the continuous, on-line solution of six, non-linear differential equations.

Having introduced in some detail the aspect of simulation it is natural to consider the potentiality of the d.d.a. for more extensive work of this kind. G. C. Rowley deals with the simultaneous d.d.a. in this context and concentrates attention on those properties an integrator should possess to work in a large assembly of integrators and in a form exactly comparable with operational amplifiers and function generators.

So far the d.d.a. has been dealt with as a third machine lying between the g.p. and analogue computers. However, it is possible for a d.d.a. to exist as a section of a g.p. computer [24]. By this is meant not that the g.p. computer is programmed to simulate the d.d.a. but that certain areas of the working store of the computer are permanently allocated to the d.d.a. section to form the Y and R registers in association with areas of logic for mechanization of the integration process.

It is then possible, by the use of conventional g.p. programming to insert data into the d.d.a. registers, to inter-connect integrators and to control start and stop times under g.p. control. This technique forms the basis of Chapter 8 in which K. S. White describes the real-time, on-line computations in airborne navigation.

Appendices A and B are two studies done on a fifty-integrator [16] sequential d.d.a. with an iteration rate of 500 per second. The first by E. Wagner is the simulation of a symmetrical fault applied to a high-voltage grid system and the second by P. L. Owen is an exercise in machine tool control. These, together with the preceding chapters, illustrate the wide field of application of the d.d.a.. In fact the emphasis throughout this book is on theory and application to show just how a d.d.a. can be used. There is no descriptive matter on the components or the electronic techniques used in various machines but care has been taken to ensure that the references are comprehensive in this respect.

The material in each chapter is based on the binary number system with 2's complement representation of negative numbers thus allowing a uniform approach by all the authors. There are, of course, decimal and octal machines as well as the d.d.a.'s used with g.p.'s where methods of input and output are in an appropriate code. Again references are given where relevant.

It is fitting to end this opening chapter with a direct quotation from Babbage [23]:

> 'It will be an interesting question which time only can solve, to know whether tables or cards will even be required by the Engine. Tables are used for saving the time of continually computing individual numbers. But the computations to be made by the Engine are so rapid that it seems most probable that it will make shorter work by computing directly from proper formulae than by having recourse to even its own Tables'.

Babbage's reference to proper formulae is singularly apt as is his remark about the time wasted in computation of individual numbers; we are of the opinion that Babbage would have been pleased with the d.d.a.

References

[1] WILLIAMS, R. W. (1961) *Analogue Computation*, Heywood.

[2] WILKES, M. V. (1956) *Automatic Digital Computers*, Methuen.

[3] THOMSON, J. (Feb. 1876) 'On an Integrating Machine having a new Kinematic Principle', *Proc. Roy. Soc.*, **24**.

[4] THOMSON, SIR W. (May 1878) 'Harmonic Analyser', *Proc. Roy. Soc.*, **27**.

[5] BUSH, V. (Oct. 1931) 'The Differential Analyser', *J. Franklin Inst.*, 212, No. 4, 447–488.

[6] AMBLE, O. (Dec. 1946) 'On a Principle of Connexion for Bush Integrators', *J. Sci. Instr.*, 284–287.

[7] CRANK, J. (1947) *The Differential Analyser*, Longmans, Green.

[8] GILBERT, C. P. (1964) *The Design and Use of Electronic Analogue Computers*, Chapman & Hall.

[9] HURNEY, P. A. JR. (Feb. 1956) 'Combined Analog and Digital Techniques for the Solution of Differential Equations', *Proc. Western Joint Computer Conf.*, San Francisco, 64–68.

[10] MILLER, D. R., GRADO, G. N. and BAKER, B. R. (July 1965) 'Ci-5000 Hybrid Computing System', *Simulation*.

[11] DONAN, J. F. (April 1952) 'The Serial Memory D.D.A.' Mathematical Tables and Other Aids to Computation. **6**, No. 38, 102–112.

[12] MENDELSON, M. J. (Feb. 1954) 'The Decimal Digital D.A.' *Aeron. Eng. Rev.*, **13**, No. 2, 42–54.

[13] PALEVSKY, M. (October 1953) 'The Design of the Bendix D.D.A.', *Proc. I.R.E.*, **41**, No. 10, 1352–1386.

[14] —, (March 1961) 'Maddida, Magnetic Drum D.A.', *Electronics*.

[15] RUHMAN, S. and MITCHELL, J. (1958) 'The Trice, A High Speed Incremental Computer', *I.R.E. Nat. Conv. Record*, Pt. 4, 206–216.

[16] MILLINGTON, K. (April 1959) 'The Incremental Computer (D.D.A.), An Experimental Model'. *Tech. Note* MS 54, Royal Aircraft Establishment, Farnborough, England.

[17] OWEN, P. L., PARTRIDGE, M. F., SIZER, T. R. H., (August 1961) 'A Transistor D.D.A.' *J. Brit. I.R.E.*, **22** No. 2.

[18] OWEN, P. L. PARTRIDGE, M. F. and SIZER, T. R. H. (October & November 1960), 'The Differential Analyser and its Realisation in Digital Form', *Elect. Eng.* **32**, 614–7, 700–4.

[19] LEONDES, C. T. (1961) *Computer Control Systems Technology*, McGraw Hill, N.Y.

[20] MISHKIN, E. and BRAUN, L. (1961) *Adaptive Control Systems*, McGraw Hill, N.Y.

[21] MONROE, A. J. (1962), *Digital Processes for Sampled Data Systems*, Wiley, N.Y.

[22] SIZER, T. R. H. (January 1962) 'An Arithmetic Unit made with Surface Barrier Transistors in Direct Coupled Logic', *Tech. Note* IAP 1118. Royal Aircraft Establishment, Farnborough, England.

[23] DREW, D. R. 'Analysis of Simulation of Incremental Computations Performed by Binary Rate Multipliers' *MIT Report* 7849-R-10.

[24] PAYNE, W. R. (October 1961) 'DEXAN – a Digital Experimental Airborne Navigator', *World Aviation Electronics*, 113–116.

[25] BABBAGE, H. P. (1889) *Babbage's Calculating Engines*, Spon.

2: The Principles of Incremental Representation

2.1 Introduction

Digital numbers always change in discrete steps and consequently continuously variable analogue quantities cannot be represented exactly in digital form. It is necessary to decide on an accuracy of representation. For example, if a variable is to be represented to 1 per cent accuracy the total range of variation must be divided into 100 equal steps and the representation at any given time may only take one of 101 discrete values, a point illustrated in Figure 2.1 which shows the digitization of a quantity to 10 per cent accuracy.

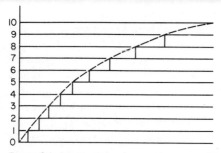

Figure 2.1. Digitization of an analogue quantity to 10 per cent accuracy.

Eleven equally spaced horizontal lines are superimposed on the graph of the variable and the numbers 0–10 are associated with these lines. Then the digital representation of the quantity at any time is the number associated with the nearest line below. It may be seen that the representation is only exact at certain instances, for the rest of the time it has an error known as 'round-off'. Another way of associating the number with the quantity is to take the nearest line which may be above or below. This method of round-off is more accurate since the maximum error is only half the distance between two lines as compared with the first method in which the maximum error is the complete distance.

The change in the variable corresponding to the difference between two consecutive levels is the smallest change which may be represented digitally and is known as the quantum. The quantum is always represented by one unit in the position of least significance in the digital number.

The second way in which the digital quantity differs from an analogue quantity is brought about by the nature of the digital machine. Unlike the analogue computer the digital machine is unable to compute its output continuously in time. The operations in a digital computer are necessarily discrete – consisting of multiplications and additions etc. which produce unique answers. Hence the nearest the digital computer can get to dealing with continuous quantities is to sample the inputs and compute the corresponding outputs. This must be repeated as frequently as possible to produce a succession of values of the outputs. It is thus possible to associate with a digital computer a fundamental period of time known as the 'iteration period' which is the time taken to sample all the inputs and compute all the outputs once. Having sampled the inputs during one iteration cycle the computer is unable to take account of any change until the next cycle. Thus the iteration period can be regarded as the quantum of time. So it can be said that in a digital computer the variables are quantized both in magnitude and time.

The main requirements for a digital computer to perform analogue type problems are now clear. While the digital process is inherently accurate, the nature of the representation is that errors will be present because of the two effects which have been described but the finer the quantization and the faster the solution rate the more accurate is the representation which is obtained. Thus, the type of digital computer necessary to solve analogue type problems must be able to represent the variables sufficiently accurately and have a sufficiently high solution rate.

Accuracy of representation may be achieved by taking a sufficient number of binary places and, in principle, presents no difficulty. For the conventional general purpose computer with a stored program, however, solution rate is dependent on the complexity of the problem being solved. Typical rates with present day computer speeds range from 1–20 per second. Some problems, however, require much higher solution rates and new approaches are necessary. One such avenue is the use of incremental techniques which leads to the concept of the digital differential analyser. It will be shown in the next section that substantial increases in solution rate may be achieved thereby.

2.2 Absolute and incremental computation

In the investigation of physical systems one is interested in the behaviour of the variables as a function of time and this is achieved in the general purpose digital computer by calculating a succession of values at discrete moments in time. The conventional digital computer approach is to calculate each value completely independently of any of the previously calculated values. Now an important property of a physical system is that it behaves in a continuous manner, in other words it changes by only a small amount in a small interval of time. Thus, knowing the state at one instant of time it is only necessary to calculate a small change which occurs during an iteration period to obtain the state at the next instant. Since the change is always small it would seem reasonable to expect that the calculation of the change is simpler and hence may be performed more frequently than the calculation of the absolute value from the initial conditions each time. That, in fact, this is so is shown by the following two examples of typical calculations in which the absolute and incremental methods are compared. It is assumed for the basis of comparison that the arithmetic speeds are equal.

Consider as the first example the case of ordinary multiplication of two 13 digit binary number. The absolute method would be to use the usual long multiplication algorithm of successive additions. In this case 13 additions would be necessary. Using the incremental approach, however, one would proceed as follows:

Suppose that the value of the product is known at a given instant of time:

$$Z = XY$$

and it is wished to calculate the value after one iteration period during which X and Y have changed to $X + \delta X$ and $Y + \delta Y$ respectively. The new value of the product is:

$$(X + \delta X)(Y + \delta Y) = XY + X\,\delta Y + Y\,\delta X + \delta X\,\delta Y\;.$$

Assuming that the values of the increments are sufficiently small that one may ignore the second order term, the change in the product is then:

$$X\,\delta Y + Y\,\delta X$$

and this is the increment which must be calculated.

At first sight it would appear that the computation task has been made greater since two multiplications and one addition are necessary to obtain the next value of the product. However, if by suitable scaling and sufficiently short iteration period each of the variables never changes by more than one quantum or, in other words, δX and δY are limited to the values $\frac{1}{2}^n$, 0, or $-\frac{1}{2}^n$, where n defines the size of the quantum, then the two increments are of the form $\pm X/2^n$ and $\pm Y/2^n$. Thus the new value of the product may be obtained from the old value by merely adding or subtracting X and Y at a suitable level of significance. Hence using the incremental method an amount of computation which is not greater than two additions is required for each step. Comparison with the conventional computer approach shows that a gain in speed of 6·5 to 1 has been obtained.

For the next example consider the computation of the trigonometrical functions $\sin \theta$ and $\cos \theta$. The conventional approach is to express the function as a polynomial or series expansion and evaluate this by arithmetic methods. For 13 binary places it is sufficient to take an expression of the form:

$$\sin \theta = A\theta + B\theta^3 + C\theta^5 .$$

Starting with θ, two multiplications are necessary to get θ^3 and another to get θ^5. Three further multiplications are necessary to introduce the constants A, B, and C, and finally two additions to obtain the complete expression. Taking, as before, a multiplication as equivalent to 13 additions, 93 additions are necessary for $\sin \theta$ and 93 for $\cos \theta$, making a total of 186 for the two functions.

The increments to the functions may be obtained by writing:

$$\sin(\theta + \delta\theta) = \sin \theta + \delta\theta \cos \theta$$
$$\cos(\theta + \delta\theta) = \cos \theta - \delta\theta \sin \theta .$$

Thus, knowing the values of $\sin \theta$ and $\cos \theta$ and assuming as before that $\delta\theta$ is never greater in magnitude than one quantum, it is only necessary to add or subtract $\cos \theta$ and $\sin \theta$ at some suitable level of significance to the old values to obtain the new values. Hence the amount of computation per step is never more than two additions if the incremental approach is taken. One, therefore gets an increase in speed of $93:1$.

These examples show clearly the increase in speed that may be obtained by incremental methods. Similar arguments can be produced for any particular problem to show the gain in speed from the incremental approach. In practice the increase in speed would not be so great as indicated above since there are techniques available for speeding up general purpose computation also. Examples are: the use of a multiplication algorithm which cuts down on the number of additions required, and the use of nesting and Chebychev polynomials for the computation of transcendental functions. Nevertheless, even though these techniques are taken into account, it is still true that a substantial increase in solution rate may be achieved by the use of incremental methods. This is borne out by the present existence of incremental machines which are capable of solving complex simulation problems at solution rates of up to several thousand per second.

2.3 The digital integrator

In the examples of computation by incremental methods it will have been noted that the mathematical expressions calculated are of the form $Y\,\delta X$.

For instance, in the calculation of sin θ and cos θ, the increments were cos $\theta\,\delta\theta$ and $-\sin\theta\,\delta\theta$ respectively. Similarly, for multiplication, one calculated $X\,\delta Y$ and $Y\,\delta X$ and added these to form the complete increment $X\,\delta Y + Y\,\delta X$. It will be shown later in Chapter 3, in which programming and scaling are considered in detail, that all incremental operations may be reduced to expressions of this form. Assuming, then, that such expressions are sufficient for dealing with any incremental problem it will now be shown how they may be calculated. An important point to remember, however, is that the answer to the problem is obtained by accumulating the increments and consequently one is really interested in expressions of the form:

$$\Sigma Y . \delta X .$$

Since one of the fundamental premises is that the increment δX is always small, this expression is a close approximation to the integral $\int Y\,\delta X$ and for this reason in this book the device which evaluates such expressions is termed an integrator. Any integration which is required for the problem is, in fact, performed by making use of this approximation.

To show how such an integrator may be constructed in digital form it is convenient to start with the simple case of integration with respect to time in which all the δX's are constant and then proceed to the general case later.

Figure 2.2 shows the behaviour of a typical quantity as a function of time. Each horizontal step is one iteration period of the process and each vertical step is a unit in the magnitude of the function. During one iteration period the change in the integral is the area of the corresponding rectangle $Y\,\delta T$ and if these areas are accumulated the result is the integral of the quantity with respect to time, i.e.

$$\Sigma Y\,\delta T \text{ which is an approximation to } \int Y\,\mathrm{d}T .$$

Now, since the iteration period is the quantum of time it is represented as one unit digitally and hence the area of the rectangle is numerically equal to

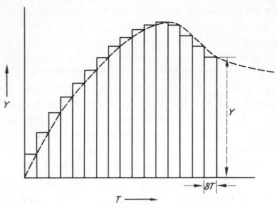

Figure 2.2. Integration with respect to time.

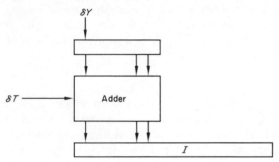

Figure 2.3. Digital integrator with respect to time.

its height. Keeping this in mind it is now possible to describe a digital device which performs the operation of integration with respect to time. Figure 2.3 shows a digital integrator and it may be seen to consist of two digital registers called the Y and I registers. The Y register always holds the current value of the height of the curve, usually referred to as the 'integrand'. During each iteration period two operations take place:

(i) The Y number is brought up to date, represented by Y^*, by adding the increment in Y:

$$Y^* = Y + \delta Y .$$

(ii) The current value of Y is added to the I number to form the current value of the integral:

$$I^* = I + Y^* .$$

It may be noted that the Y number is changed by adding an increment. In principle the whole Y number could be changed at each step but this would be a departure from the incremental philosophy and would result in a loss of speed. In addition to this, the design of a d.d.a. may be much simplified by transferring increments rather than whole numbers.

The process of digital integration with respect to time has been seen to be a simple operation and it is now necessary to consider the more general case of integration with respect to any variable. In the process of integration with respect to time the Y number is multiplied by the time increment, in this case one quantum or unit, and added to the I number to bring it up to date. In the case of a variable other than time whose increment is δX, say, it is only necessary to multiply the Y number or integrand by δX and add it to the I number to obtain the current value of the integral. In general this implies that the addition process be replaced by a multiplication and addition as indicated by the equation:

$$I^* = I + Y^* \delta X .$$

It has, however, been shown that the more general type of integration may be considerably simplified if the rate of the X input is limited so that in any iteration period the change in X is never greater than one quantum or unit either positive or negative. The implications of this become more apparent in Chapter 3 on scaling and programming; it is sufficient at this stage to state that δX may only take three values, viz.: $+1, 0, -1$, and the necessity for a full multiplication is removed. The rules for the integration process now become:

    (i) Add Y if δX is 1.
    (ii) Subtract if δX is -1.
    (iii) Do nothing if δX is 0.

The digital integrator takes the form shown in Figure 2.4 in which the adder is replaced by a transfer device controlled by δX and adds or subtracts the value of Y or does nothing according to the value of δX.

In order to use integrators to solve problems it is essential that they can be interconnected, but as described so far the integrator is not in quite the required form for interconnection since all the inputs are in incremental form whereas the output, i.e. the integral, is in whole number form in the I register. In order to be able to connect it to the inputs of other integrators it is necessary to produce the increments of the integral rather than the whole number form.

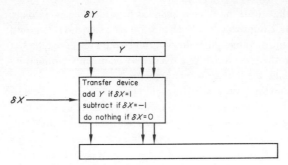

Figure 2.4. The general digital integrator.

To see how this may be done it is convenient to take a simple numerical example Figure 2.5. For the sake of simplicity consider the integrand takes only the values from 0–9. As a function of time the integrand is given in the first column. Considering the simple case of time integration, successive additions of the integrand give the numbers in the second column which are the contents of the *I* register.

Y	I		R		Integral
4	4		4		0
5	9		9		0
6	1	5	5	Overflow	1
6	2	1	1	Overflow	2
7	2	8	8		2
8	3	6	6	Overflow	3
8	4	4	4	Overflow	4
8	5	2	2	Overflow	5
8	6	0	0	Overflow	6
8	6	8	8		6

Figure 2.5. Numerical example of digital integration.

It may be noted that while the integrand consists only of a single integer the integral very soon builds up to a double figure number. In other words the *I* register must be able to contain more digits than the *Y* register. It is possible here to draw a parallel with the process of long multiplication in which two quantities of a given number of digits are multiplied to give a product with twice the number of digits. For instance, 8 times 9 equals 72, each factor consists of one digit while the product consists of two digits. In physical calculations the normal procedure is to take the most significant half of the answer as being all that is warranted by the accuracy of the inputs. (Multiplication using four figure logarithms only gives an answer to four figures and not to eight figures.) Thus the part of the I number of interest is the most significant half and this represents the value of the integral to some scale. In Figure 2.5 a dotted line is drawn separating the two halves of the I number and the measure of the integral is given by the number on the left-hand side of the line.

Thus in the digital integrator the I register may be divided into two halves as shown in Figure 2.6 and the number in the right-hand half may be taken as the value of the integral. If now the right-hand half is removed completely and the register, now called the R register, contains the same number of digits as the Y register, the effect of the successive addition of Y numbers to the R number will cause it to overflow periodically. These overflows occur at the same time as the number in the upper half increases by one and conse-quently they are the increments of the integral.

The last three columns in Figure 2.5 illustrate the process, showing the values of the R numbers, the positions of the overflows and the values of the in-

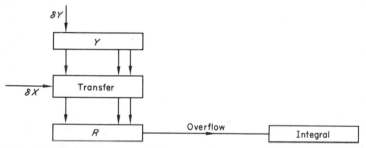

Figure 2.6. Digital integrator with incremental output.

tegral respectively. Thus by cutting the length of the I register a device has been produced which has inputs and outputs in incremental form and hence may be connected with other such devices. This method of producing incre-ments is clearly not confined to time as the independent variable; it works just as well when integrating with respect to other variables with the addi-tional feature that negative increments may occur also.

To sum up, the final form of the integrator which is used in the d.d.a. is a device consisting of two equal length registers, Y and R. The Y number is kept up to date by the addition of increments according to the equation:

$$Y^* = Y + \delta Y$$

at each step.

The current value of Y is multiplied by the X increment, δX, which in the ternary d.d.a. only takes the values 1, 0, and -1, and is then added to the number in the R register. The result of this operation is to cause the R number to overflow periodically, the overflows representing the increments of the integral as shown by the equation:

$$R + Y^* . \delta X = R^* + \delta Z$$

where δZ is a convenient notation for the overflow.

The two inputs to the integrator are increments of the integrand and independent variable respectively and these may be connected to the outputs of other integrators to form flow diagrams as shown in subsequent chapters. The X increment has the limitation that it must take the values 1, 0, or -1, but the Y increment is not so limited. In terms of integrators it means that while there is no restriction to the number of inputs which may be connected to the Y register, only one may be connected to the δX input. If the form of the problem necessitates connecting more than one input to δX it is possible to use an intermediate integrator to accomplish this. The technique is fully described in Chapter 3.

2.4 Binary and ternary transfer

It is now clear that the transfer of information between integrators takes place in the form of increments whose absolute magnitude is never greater than one bit or quantum. In the schemes so far discussed this increment has been capable of taking three values, viz.: 0, $+1$, and -1. A three-level increment scheme is known as a ternary transfer system. It is, however, possible to have two level schemes in which the increment may only take the values $+1$ and -1. This is equally capable of describing the behaviour of a function, and in particular, zero rate of change would be represented by the sequence $+1$, -1, $+1$, -1, ... etc. A two-level scheme is known as a binary transfer system.

Whichever mode is used, the action of the digital integrator is substantially the same. Ternary transfer is assumed in the early chapters for the sake of clarity. Reference to machines using the binary transfer mode has been made in Chapter 1 and Chapter 8 is based on the use of such a machine.

2.5 The binary rate multiplier

Before passing to the general organization of the digital differential analyser it is of interest to mention an alternative form of the digital integrator known as the binary rate multiplier. This device is sometimes used in numerical and process control and, subject to certain restrictions which will become apparent later, is suitable to form the basic element of a digital differential analyser.

Functionally, this unit behaves in exactly the same way as the $Y \ R$ type of integrator, but its mode of operation is quite different. Referring to Figure 2.7 it will be seen that the Y number is held in a binary register and it may be varied by adding or subtracting increments. Each stage of the register is connected to an AND gate, the other input of which is a pulse train whose frequency is f (the input frequency) divided by an appropriate power of 2. Taking the most significant end of the Y register to be on the left the fre-

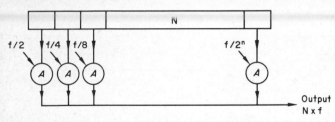

Figure 2.7. *The binary rate multiplier.*

quencies are as shown in Figure 2.7. The outputs of the AND gates are fed into a common channel which is the output of the rate multiplier.

A binary number N in the Y register opens the gates associated with the stages containing the digit 1 to allow the corresponding pulse train to pass to the output line. Provided there is no coincidence of pulses the output line then transmits the sum of the pulses which have been fed into it to give an output frequency of $N \times f$. The parallel with the Y–R type of integrator can now be seen by taking f to correspond with the ΔX pulse train, N to correspond with the Y number and the output $N \times f$ to correspond with the $Y \Delta X$ or ΔZ pulse train.

A simple binary counter whose inputs is f is used to generate the frequencies $f/2, f/4, \ldots$ etc. To obtain non-coincidence of the pulses a differentiating circuit is attached to the output of each stage of the counter which emits pulses when the corresponding stage changes from 0 to 1. That these outputs give streams with the required properties may be seen on reference to Figure 2.8 which illustrates the case of a four-digit counter. Starting with the counter at 0000 it can be seen that the first (least significant) stage changes from 0 to 1 on the first, third, fifth, seventh, etc. input pulses giving an output frequency of $f/2$. The second stage changes from 0 to 1 on the second, sixth, tenth, and fourteenth input pulses to produce an output frequency of $f/4$. The third stage changes from 0 to 1 on the fourth and twelfth input pulses to give a frequency of $f/8$, and the fourth stage changes from 0 to 1 on the eighth input pulse. Thus the transitions from 0 to 1 of the various stages of the counter determine a set of pulse streams which have the required frequencies and no coincidences.

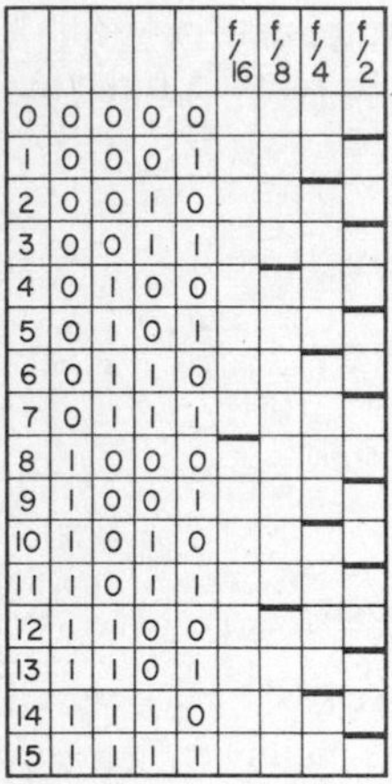

					$\frac{f}{16}$	$\frac{f}{8}$	$\frac{f}{4}$	$\frac{f}{2}$
0	0	0	0	0				
1	0	0	0	1				
2	0	0	1	0				
3	0	0	1	1				
4	0	1	0	0				
5	0	1	0	1				
6	0	1	1	0				
7	0	1	1	1				
8	1	0	0	0				
9	1	0	0	1				
10	1	0	1	0				
11	1	0	1	1				
12	1	1	0	0				
13	1	1	0	1				
14	1	1	1	0				
15	1	1	1	1				

Figure 2.8. *Generation of pulse streams.*

The binary rate multiplier is subject to certain types of errors which do not occur in the $Y–R$ type of integrator. An extreme case of this obtains if the Y number is oscillating between the values 100 ... 0 and 011 ... 1 at the input frequency f. If the phase of this oscillation is such that it takes the value 100 ... 0 on the even input pulses then no pulses can get through any of the AND gates and zero output results. Similarly, if it takes the value 1000 ... 0 on the odd input pulses then all the pulses get through to give full-rate output. The actual output should clearly be very close to $f/2$ since the Y register is oscillating about the half-full position. Thus very large errors occur for this type of input and it is clear that similar errors can occur for other input patterns. To avoid this error completely it is necessary to restrict the rate of change of the Y number so that Y remains constant for at least one complete scan of the input pulse divider, i.e. for 2^n input pulses.

For simple applications, for example a single integration with respect to time in a numerical control application, it would be feasible to impose such a restriction to give a device somewhat inferior in performance to the $Y-R$ integrator. General use, involving multiple integrator schematics and integration with respect to variables other than time, poses a much greater organizational problem. For this reason it is not proposed to deal further in this book with the binary rate multiplier as the basic element in the digital differential analyser.

2.6 The general organization of the d.d.a.

A set of digital integrators together with facilities for interconnection and input/output is known as a digital differential analyser or d.d.a. The interconnection system enables increments to be transferred between integrators and integrator schematics may be set up to solve problems in much the same way as in analogue computers.

As was mentioned in Chapter 1, there are two main ways in which d.d.a.'s may be organized. There is the type in which each integrator is a self-contained unit. The Y and R numbers are kept in two registers and each integrator has its own adder/subtractor or arithmetic unit, the integration process taking place simultaneously in all the integrators. This type of d.d.a. is known as 'simultaneous'.

In the other type the Y and R numbers are kept in a central store and read out in turn to undergo the integration process in a common arithmetic unit. This is known as the sequential type of d.d.a. since the output increments must be stored and be available at any point in the computing cycle or iteration period. Each type will now be considered in more detail.

2.7 The sequential d.d.a.

The time taken to perform a given computation is divided into a number of iteration periods as shown in Figure 2.9. A typical figure of 500 steps per

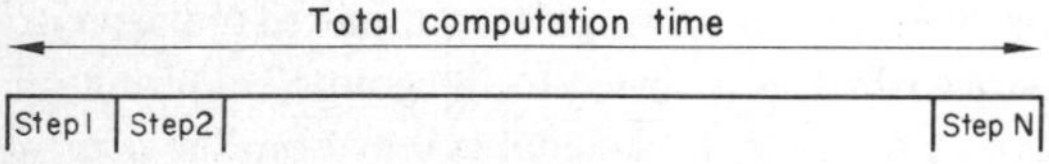

Figure 2.9. *Timing of a given computation.*

second gives a total number of iteration periods of 500 T, where T is the computation time in seconds. During each step or iteration period all the Y and R numbers are brought in turn to undergo the integration process. The periods associated with the various integrators may conveniently be labelled $I_1, I_2, \ldots I_n$ where n is the number of integrators. Thus each iteration period is divided up into n integrator periods and during the period I_i the I_i'th integrator is processed. At the beginning of each period the appropriate increments in the integrand and the independent variable must be available for the integration process.

If there is more than one integrator connected to the Y input, quite frequently the case, then more than one overflow or increment may appear at this during the same step. These increments must be added together to form the total Y increment, a process usually done by accumulation in a counter

I_1	I_2 I_3 - - - - -	I_{j-1}	I I_{j+1} - - - -	I_n
Accumulate increments for I_2		Accumulate increments for I_j		Accumulate increments for I_1
Process I_1		Process I_{j-1}		Process I_n
Transmit overflow δZ_1 to ΔZ store		Transmit δZ_{j-1} to ΔZ store		Transmit δZ_n to ΔZ store

Figure 2.10. *The timing within an iteration period of a sequential d.d.a.*

during the previous integrator period. There is thus a certain amount of overlapping of operation which increases the speed of operation. At the end of the integration period the resulting overflow or integrator output becomes available. This is transmitted to an overflow, or ΔZ, store. Figure 2.10 shows the timing in the iteration period.

Integrator interconnections may be most conveniently illustrated by an example. Suppose, for instance, that it is required to connect the input of integrator 5 to the output of integrator 1. The operation is as follows. At the end of integrator period I_1 the δZ output from integrator 1 becomes available as a result of the integration process and is transmitted to the physical position in the ΔZ store which is assigned to integrator 1. During the period immediately previous to I_5, i.e. I_4, a signal is sent from the control unit which extracts δZ_1 and stores it temporarily. It is then available for insertion into the appropriate input of integrator 5 during I_5. If more than one integrator is to be connected to integrator 5, say integrators 1, 10, and 12, the overflows δZ_1, δZ_{10} and δZ_{12} are extracted in sequence and accumulated in the counter in period I_4 so that the total increment is available for period I_5. The process is illustrated in Figure 2.11.

I_1	I_2	I_3	I_4	I_5	I_6	I_7…	I_8	I_9	I_{10}	I_{11}	I_{12}	ETC
Process I_1 and send δZ_1 to ΔZ store			Select $\delta Z_1, \delta Z_{10}$ and δZ_{12} from ΔZ store and accumulate to form complete Y increment	Add increment to Y to form Y^* add Y^* to r to produce δZ_5					Process I_{10} send δZ_{10} to ΔZ store		Process I_{12} send δZ_{12} to ΔZ store	

Figure 2.11. *Timing for connecting outputs of I_1, I_{10}, I_{12} to Y input of I_5.*

The general organization of the sequential d.d.a. is shown in Figure 2.12. It may be seen to consist of four main units, viz.: the main store for the Y and R numbers, the arithmetic unit, the increment or ΔZ store, and the programming or control unit. During each integrator period the associated Y–R number pair is read out of the main store into the arithmetic unit where it under-

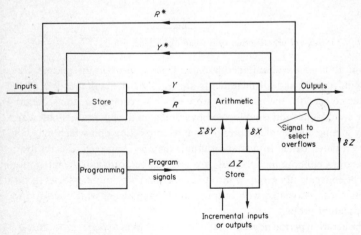

Figure 2.12. *General organization of a sequential d.d.a.*

goes the integration process. The resulting overflow which appears at the end of the period is selected and transmitted to the appropriate position in the ΔZ store while the new Y and R numbers, Y^* and R^*, are returned to the main store. Meanwhile in the programming unit the appropriate increments are extracted to be accumulated for the next integrator period.

There are also facilities for inputs and outputs which may be of two kinds, whole number or incremental. Whole number inputs and outputs are always Y numbers; inputs are usually inserted into the main store but outputs may come from the arithmetic unit or the main store. Incremental inputs are most conveniently inserted into the ΔZ store while the outputs may either come from the ΔZ store or they could be the overflows resulting from the integration process.

2.8 The simultaneous d.d.a.

The organization of the simultaneous d.d.a. is much simpler in principle than that of the sequential d.d.a. For a constant digit rate the iteration speed is independent of the number of integrators. Figure 2.13 shows the general

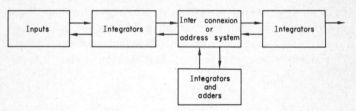

Figure 2.13. *General organization of a simultaneous d.d.a.*

organization of the simultaneous d.d.a. Operation of all integrators takes place in parallel and all increments are transferred simultaneously. There is thus no need for the increment store which is required for the sequential d.d.a. Interconnection is performed by joining up the integrators physically, or by joining all the integrators to an interconnection unit which may consist of a patch panel. Inputs and outputs may be connected directly to the integrators, either in incremental or whole number form and the integrators may be conveniently grouped into three sections, viz.: those associated with inputs, those associated with outputs and the remainder which perform the computation proper.

The iteration period now consists of the time it takes to perform one integration process and this is divided into two phases: the first consisting of the

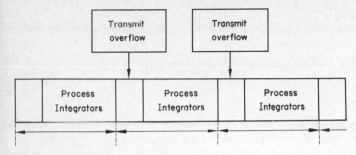

Figure 2.14. *Timing of a simultaneous d.d.a.*

transmission of all the overflows or increments to their appropriate inputs, and the second consisting of the actual integration process. Figure 2.14 illustrates the timing of events for the simultaneous d.d.a. The principle is developed more fully in Chapter 7.

3: The Principles of Programming

3.1 The integrator

The principles of the integrator have been dealt with in Chapter 2; here it is treated in greater detail and from the point of view of programming which follows common practice in consisting of flow charting and scaling.

In flow charts the integrator is represented diagrammatically as shown in Figure 3.1. Typically, so far as inputs are concerned, there will be one ΔX

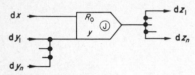

Figure 3.1. *The integrator.*

point, dx, and a ΔY point capable of accepting dy_1, dy_2, dy_3, ... etc., also, typically, there will be one ΔZ output point, 'dz' providing several equivalent outputs dz. Although several dy inputs and dz outputs are shown in Figure 3.1, normally only those actually used in a program are shown on a flow chart. A ring on the output point of an integrator, Figure 3.2, signifies that the sign

Figure 3.2. *Integrator with sign change.*

of the output is changed from $+dz$ to $-dz$ for all the dz lines originating from that element.

Each integrator is defined by a unique number, j, encircled ⓙ in the diagram and referred to in the text as (j). Thus $(1, 2, 3)$ represents integrators 1, 2 and 3 and (123) represents integrator 123. For convenience, integrators will be numbered from 1 upwards.

3.2 The number scale

The number scale of the Y register may be closed, counting in the sequence:

$$0, 1, 2, \ldots N-1, \, -N, \, -N+1, \ldots -2, \, -1, \, 0,$$

where N is a positive integer. N will in general be taken as a power of 2 i.e. binary representation. The unit by which an integrator counts will be termed an increment. When an integrator contains $N-1$, the addition of a single increment to the Y register will cause it to overflow.

Some programmers may prefer to count in fractional form and then the largest negative value a register may contain is -1. The largest positive value is $(N-1)/N$.

Increments of machine time, ΔT the independent variable, can be made available to every integrator each time is processed. The number of times the integrator can be processed in one second is the maximum rate at which increments can occur and this is called full machine rate.

3.3 The flow diagram

When a problem is presented for solution on a d.d.a., it will be in the form of a differential equation or possibly several simultaneous differential equations. These equations will have to be arranged in a suitable form.

Now the input to the Y register of an integrator is incremental and represents the derivative of the quantity in that register. Consequently the rearrangement of the equations must be such that the new version contains all the derivatives of all the original constituent variables. An example will demonstrate this re-arrangement.

Consider the second-order differential equation:

$$\frac{d^2 y}{dx^2} + A \frac{dy}{dx} + By = 0. \tag{1}$$

If a solution is required for y and dy/dx they must each be held as the Y register content of an integrator. The ΔY inputs to these two integrators are the respective derivatives of y and dy/dx, namely dy and $d(dy/dx)$. The relationship between dy and $d(dy/dx)$ is found from the original equation. Re-writing this equation with the highest-order derivative on one side and the rest of its terms on the other, the result is:

$$\frac{d^2 y}{dx^2} = -A \frac{dy}{dx} - By \tag{2}$$

or
$$\frac{d}{dx}\left(\frac{dy}{dx}\right) = -A\frac{dy}{dx} - By \tag{3}$$

since
$$dy = \frac{dy}{dx}.dx. \tag{4}$$

Multiplying the equation by dx gives:

$$d\left(\frac{dy}{dx}\right) = -A\,dy - By\,dx \tag{5}$$

which is the required equation linking dy and $d(dy/dx)$.

If there are more variables and more than one equation is required to be solved, this procedure is repeated for each equation and the links between all the variables found.

The flow diagram which shows pictorially the integrators used to obtain a solution and their interconnections can now be constructed. The quantities contained in the Y registers and the inputs and outputs of the respective integrators are all labelled in the diagram. Figure 3.3 gives the flow diagram for equation (5). Arrowheads show the direction of flow of information.

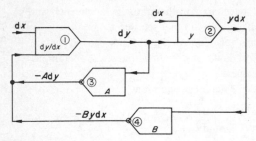

Figure 3.3. *Differential equation.*

The constants A and B are held in (3, 4) which therefore have no ΔY input. The ΔY input of (2) is $dy = dx.(dy/dx)$ which is the ΔZ output of (1). This is also the ΔX input to (3) which has a ΔZ output $-A\,dy$. The ΔZ output of (2) is $y\,dx$ which is the ΔX input of (4) giving a ΔZ output of $-By\,dx$. The rings on the outputs of (3, 4) denote the sign changes. The ΔZ outputs of (3, 4) are added together to form the ΔY input of (1) in accordance with the equation to be solved.

3.4 Scaling

After completion of the flow diagram the problem can be scaled. This is somewhat different from scaling a whole number digital computer although the basic concept of avoiding unwanted overflows still exists.

As with most computer problems either analogue or digital, the programmer first obtains some idea of the range and accuracy of the variables and the speed required in the calculation (e.g. whether it should proceed in real time). Sometimes the conditions for the solution conflict and one of then will have to be relaxed in favour of the others.

3.4.1 *Scaling constants*

The scaling constants are defined in the following way. Variables x, y, z, in the problem are represented by variables X, Y, Z, in the machine known as the machine variables. The two sets of variables are related by the equation:

$$\left. \begin{array}{l} x = XK_x \\ y = YK_y \\ z = ZK_z \end{array} \right\} \qquad (6)$$

so that K_x, K_y, K_z, represent the change in x, y, z, respectively produced by one increment. K_x, K_y, K_z, are known as the scale constants and if the dimensions of all the variables occurring in an equation are consistent then the machine variables and scale constants defined above will also be consistent.

3.4.2 *Integrator equations*

Suppose an integrator (j) has problem variable inputs dx and dy for ΔX and ΔY respectively. Then the ΔZ output represented by the problem variable dx is given as:

$$dz = y\,dx \qquad (7)$$

the dy input having been integrated (or accumulated) to give y in the Y register. Now if the capacity of (j) is N_j the basic integrator equation is:

$$dz = \frac{y\,dx}{N_j} \qquad (8)$$

or taking the scale constants for (j) as k_{x_j}, k_{y_j}, k_{z_j}, equation (8) becomes:

$$\frac{dz}{K_{z_j}} = \frac{y\,dx}{K_{y_j} K_{x_j} N_j} \qquad (9)$$

in problem variables. Using equation (7) the relationship between the scaling constants can be obtained from equation (9). This is:

$$K_{z_j} = K_{x_j} K_{y_j} N_j \,. \tag{10}$$

If M_j is the value of problem variable represented by a full register:

$$M_j \geqslant y_{m_j} \tag{11}$$

y_{m_j} is the largest value of problem variable likely to occur in the computation so that the integrator capacity is governed by M_j according to the equation:

$$\frac{M_j}{K_{y_j}} = N_j \tag{12}$$

then from equation (10):

$$K_{z_j} = M_j K_{x_j} \,. \tag{13}$$

If there is a constant A in the Y register of (j) these equations will still hold but the register length for the integrator may be set at its maximum value for the computer.

3.4.3 *The scaling table*
For simple configurations, e.g. the ΔZ output being looped back as the ΔY input of an integrator, it may be necessary to solve only equation (10) in order to obtain the values of the scaling constants. Usually there is insufficient information available to solve equation (10) alone and equations (12) and (13) will have to be solved separately for each integrator in turn. A convenient way to do this is to construct a table in conjunction with the flow diagram previously completed.

The integrators will have been numbered and these numbers are transferred to the table, a line being allocated to each integrator. The table is divided up into columns which contain, reading from left to right:

The integrator's number (j).

The quantity (in problem variables) held in the Y register.

The number of the integrator (i) whose output is the source of (j)'s ΔX input, or ΔT if the ΔX source is machine time.

The numbers of the integrators whose outputs are the sources of the ΔY inputs to (j).

The maximum value that y can attain in problem variable form, y_m.

The maximum value calculated for y in machine variable form, M.

The Principles of Programming 33

The scale constant on the ΔX input, K_x.
The scale constant on the ΔZ output, K_z.
The scale constant on the ΔY input, K_y.
The register length of the integrator, N.

Integrator number	Y register content	ΔX	ΔY	y_m	M	K_x	K_z	K_y	N

The columns describing the integrator and its interconnexions can be filled in first. Any fixed values of y_m, N, or the K_x required for the ΔT input may also be inserted. Remembering that $M \geqslant y_m$, the other columns can be filled in using equations (12) and (13). Naturally not all these columns can be completed at once but, starting with the information available for each integrator, some of the K_x, K_y, K_z, can be found and then using the ΔX and ΔY columns they will be seen to correspond to certain of the K_x, K_y, or K_z of other integrators.

When all the columns have been filled the scaling is complete. It may be necessary to insert arbitrary values for some of the values of K_x, K_y, or K_z, if there is insufficient knowledge about the problem, and from there work out N and M for each integrator. If these are incorrect, e.g. $M < y_m$ then some of the K_x, K_y, K_z will have been badly chosen and must be revised accordingly.

3.4.4 A second-order differential equation
The flow diagram for the second-order differential equation:

$$\frac{d^2 y}{dx^2} + A\frac{dy}{dx} + By = 0 \tag{14}$$

has already been given in Figure 3.3. In order to scale this equation suppose $A = 0.271$ and $B = 12.3$ and assume a solution is required for $0 \leqslant x < 8$ for which y is represented to one part in 1000.

A table is drawn up with integrator numbers in order in the left-hand

Integrator number	Y register content	ΔX	ΔY	y_m	M	K_x	K_z	K_y	N
1	dy/dx	ΔT	3, 4	—	2^2	2^{-12}	2^{-10}	2^8	2^{10}
2	y	ΔT	1	—	2^0	2^{-12}	2^{-12}	2^{-10}	2^{10}
3	0.271 (A)	1	—	0.271	2^2	2^{-10}	2^{-8}	2^{2-n}	2^n
4	12.3 (B)	2	—	12.3	2^4	2^{-12}	2^{-8}	2^{4-n}	2^n

column. Next are their respective contents described in problem variables. The ΔX and ΔY columns are completed by referring to the flow diagrams. The y_m may be inserted for the constants and for the variables if known.

Now if y and dy/dz are to be represented to one part in 1000, the most convenient register capacity, N, for (1, 2) will be 1024 or 2^{10}. This will give a representation of one part in 1024. Since (3, 4) contain constants, $N_3 = N_4 = 2^n$ where 2^n is the maximum register capacity. The N column is now complete.

Consider each integrator in turn. Applying equation (10) to (1):

$$K_{z_1} = K_{x_1} K_{y_1} 2^{10} \tag{15}$$

and to (2):

$$K_{z_2} = K_{x_2} K_{y_2} 2^{10} . \tag{16}$$

Using equation (13):

$$K_{z_3} = M_3 K_{x_3} \tag{17}$$

$$K_{z_4} = M_4 K_{x_4} . \tag{18}$$

The reason for including the ΔX and ΔY columns will now become apparent. From these it can be seen that the ΔZ output of (1) is the same as the ΔY input to (2) and the ΔX input to (3). This means that the scale constants on the ΔZ of (1), the ΔY of (2) and ΔX of (3) are equal, i.e.:

$$K_{z_1} = K_{y_2} = K_{x_3} . \tag{19}$$

Similarly:

$$K_{y_1} = K_{z_3} = K_{z_4} \tag{20}$$

and

$$K_{x_4} = K_{z_2} . \tag{21}$$

Substituting for K_{x_3} and K_{z_3} in equation (17) from equations (15), (19), (20):

$$1 = 2^{10} M_3 K_{x_1}. \tag{22}$$

Substituting for K_{x_4} and K_{z_4} in equation (18) from equations (15), (16), (20), (21):

$$1 = 2^{20} M_4 K_{x_1} K_{x_2} . \tag{23}$$

Now K_{x_1} and K_{x_2} are each derived from the machine time source and therefore must be regarded as equal. Also the minimum values for M_3 and M_4 in powers of 2 may be determined. These are:

$$y_{m_3} = 0.271 \leqslant M_3 , \quad y_{m_4} = 12.3 \leqslant M_4 .$$

By comparing equations (22) and (23) it is seen that for the minimum values of M_3 and M_4 to hold together it is necessary for the most accurate representation of the constants that:

$$M_4 = 2^4, \quad K_x = 2^{-12} \quad \text{and} \quad M_3 = 2^2.$$

Substituting for K_{x_1} and K_{x_2} in equation (15) and (16), the result is:

$$K_{z_1} = 2^{-2} k_{y_1} \tag{24}$$

$$K_{z_2} = 2^{-2} k_{y_2} \tag{25}$$

$$= 2^{-4} K_{y_1}. \tag{26}$$

Using equation (13) for (1, 2):

$$M_1 2^{-12} = K_{z_1} \tag{27}$$

$$M_2 2^{-12} = K_{z_2} \tag{28}$$

which gives:

$$M_1 = 4M_2. \tag{29}$$

If the initial values for dy/dx and y are 0 and $\frac{3}{4}$ respectively, trial computations will show that suitable values for M_1 and M_2 are 4 and 1. The rest of the scaling table can now be filled in.

3.5 Simple sub-programs

This section deals with the flow diagrams and scaling of standard programs which are used in later sections of this and subsequent chapters.

3.5.1 *The exponential loop*

The differential equation for an exponential function is given as:

$$d(e^t) = e^t \, dt. \tag{30}$$

The flow diagram shown in Figure 3.4 defined by this equation with a ΔX input of dt from the machine time source of the computer, and a ΔY input

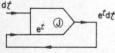

Figure 3.4. *The exponential loop.*

which is the same as the ΔZ output. Then $K_{z_j} = K_{y_j}$ and from equation (10):

$$K_{z_j} = N_j K_{x_j} K_{y_j} \tag{31}$$

or:

$$K_{x_j} = \frac{1}{N_j}. \tag{32}$$

The programmer can make an arbitrary choice for K_{y_v} but taking equation (13) and $K_{x_j} = 1/N_j$ it will be seen that the value of M_j is determined by that of K_{y_j}. By fixing the register capacity as N, M_j has a value of NK_{y_j}.

In the special case where $M_j = 1$ equation (12) becomes:

$$N_j = \frac{1}{K_{y_j}} \tag{33}$$

or

$$K_{y_j} = \frac{1}{N_j} \tag{34}$$

i.e.

$$K_{x_j} = K_{y_j} = \frac{1}{N_j}. \tag{35}$$

3.5.2 *The sin-cosine loop*

Sin θ and cos θ can be generated in the same loop by applying the differential equations:

$$d(\cos\theta) = -\sin\theta\, d\theta \tag{36}$$

$$d(\sin\theta) = \cos\theta\, d\theta. \tag{37}$$

In Figure 3.5 sin θ is contained in the Y register of (1) and cos θ is contained in the Y register of (4). The ΔZ output of (1) $-\sin\theta\, d\theta$ is the ΔY input of (4)

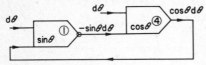

Figure 3.5. *The sin-cosine loop.*

and similarly the ΔZ output of (4), cos $\theta\, d\theta$, is the ΔY input of (1). Both ΔX inputs are $d\theta$ so have the same scale constant. Taking the capacity of each as N, then $M_1 = M_4$ and:

equation (13) gives

$$K_{z_1} = M_1 K_{x_1} \tag{38}$$

and

equation (12) gives

$$K_{y_4} = \frac{N}{M_4}. \tag{39}$$

Now $K_{z_1} = K_{y_4}$

so comparing (38) and (39):

$$K_{x_1} = \frac{1}{N}. \tag{40}$$

3.5.3 *A method of obtaining arc sin and arc cos*

Given $d(\sin \theta)$ and $d(\cos \theta)$ as two available inputs, θ may be found from them as shown in Figure 3.6 by application of the equation:

$$\cos^2 \theta + \sin^2 \theta = 1 \tag{41}$$

i.e. $$(\cos^2 \theta + \sin^2 \theta)d\theta = d\theta \tag{42}$$

i.c. $$\cos \theta \, d(\sin \theta) - \sin \theta \, d(\cos \theta) = d\theta . \tag{43}$$

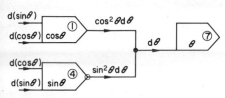

Figure 3.6. Arc sin and arc cosine.

If the scale constants on the inputs are equal to K then from equation (10):

$$K_{z_1} = K_{z_4} = NK^2 = K_{y_7} \tag{44}$$

where the capacities of $(1, 4)$ are N. If:

$$y_{m_1} = y_{m4} = 1 \quad \text{and} \quad M = \tfrac{128}{120}$$

$$K_{z_1} = \tfrac{128}{120} K = K_{z_4} \tag{45}$$

i.e. $$K_{y_7} = \tfrac{128}{120} K . \tag{46}$$

Using equations (12), M_7 and N_7 are connected by the relationship:

$$M_7 = N_7 \tfrac{128}{120} K . \tag{47}$$

3.5.4 *The product*

The flow diagram is shown in Figure 3.7,

$$d(uv) = u\,dv + v\,du . \tag{48}$$

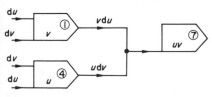

Figure 3.7. The product.

The scale constants on the outputs of the integrators containing u and v are the same, being equal to K. Then K will be the value of K_{y_7} and:

$$K = N_1 K_{x_1} K_{y_1} = N_4 K_{x_4} K_{y_4} .$$

Since $\qquad\qquad K_{x_4} K_{y_4} = K_{x_1} K_1 , \quad N_1 = N_4 = N$

3.5.5 *Generation of* x^2
The equation for the flow diagram shown in Figure 3.8 is:

$$d(x^2) = 2x\,dx . \tag{49}$$

The scaling ensures that another integrator is not required to multiply

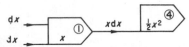

Figure 3.8. *Computation of* x^2.

$\frac{1}{2}x^2$ by 2. Instead of $K_{z_1} = K_{y_4}$ the relationship between K_{z_1} and K_{y_4} is $2K_{z_1} = K_{y_4}$.

3.5.6 *Generation of* $x^3, x^4, \ldots x^n$
This process can be repeated using:

$$d(x^n) = nx^{n-1}\,dx \tag{50}$$

to obtain x^n from x^{n-1}. The coefficient of x^n will be $1/n!$ Figure 3.9 shows the integrator connexions.

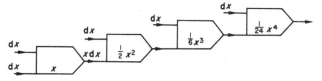

Figure 3.9. *Computation of* x^n.

3.5.7 *The reciprocal loop*
The equation for Figure 3.10 is:

$$d\left(\frac{1}{x}\right) = -\frac{1}{x^2}\,dx \tag{51}$$

$$= -\frac{1}{x}\cdot\frac{1}{x}\,dx . \tag{52}$$

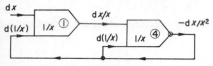

Figure 3.10. *The reciprocal loop.*

Taking $M_1 = M_4 = M$ and $N_1 = N_4 = N$, and noting:

$$K_{z_4} = K_{y_4} = K_{y_1}$$

$$K_{z_4} = K_{x_4}$$

from equation (13):

$$K_{z_1} = MK_{x_1} \tag{53}$$

$$K_{z_4} = M^2 K_{x_1} . \tag{54}$$

Using equation (12) $M/K_{y_1} = N$ and substituting:

$$1 = K_{x_1} \cdot NM \tag{55}$$

if K_{x_1} is given as K:

$$N = \frac{1}{MK} . \tag{56}$$

3.5.8 *The square root*

The flow diagram shown in Figure 3.11 is formed by the equations:

$$d(x^{\frac{1}{2}}) = \tfrac{1}{2}x^{-\frac{1}{2}}dx \tag{57}$$

$$d(x^{-\frac{1}{2}}) = -\tfrac{1}{2}x^{-\frac{3}{2}}dx \tag{58}$$

$$d(x^{-1}) = -x^{-2}dx \tag{59}$$

in which $x^{\frac{1}{2}}x^{-\frac{1}{2}}$ and x^{-1} are all generated.

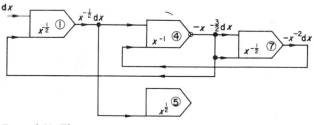

Figure 3.11. *The square root.*

$$K_{z_1} = K_{x_4} = 2K_{y_5} \tag{60}$$

$$K_{z_4} = K_{x_7} = 2K_{y_7} = 2K_{y_1} \tag{61}$$

$$K_{z_7} = K_{y_4} . \tag{62}$$

If $M_1 = M_7 = M$ and $K_{x_1} = K$ equation (13) gives:

$$K_{z_1} = MK \tag{63}$$

$$K_{z_4} = M_4 MK \tag{64}$$

$$K_{z_7} = M^2 M_4 K . \tag{65}$$

From equation (12):

$$N_1 = \frac{M}{K_{y_1}} = \frac{2}{M_4 K} = N_7$$

$$N_4 = \frac{1}{M^2 K} \quad N_5 = \frac{2M_5}{MK} .$$

3.5.9 *The quotient*

The diagram of Figure 3.12 is formed by treating

$$z = x/y \text{ as a product of } x \text{ and } 1/y \tag{66}$$

Then
$$K_{z_1} = K_{x_4} \tag{67}$$

$$K_{z_4} = K_{y_1} = K_{y_8} = K_{x_7} = K_{y_4} \tag{68}$$

$$K_{z_8} = K_{z_7} = K_{y_{11}} . \tag{69}$$

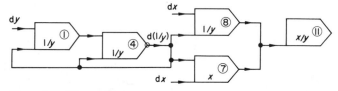

Figure 3.12. *The quotient.*

3.5.10 *Inverse of sin and cosine*

The integrator schematic for the inverse of sin is shown in Figure 3.13 and is obtained by considering:

$$u = \sin \theta \tag{70}$$

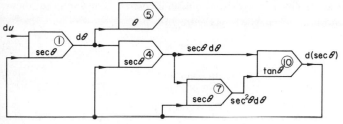

Figure 3.13. *Inverse sin.*

then
$$du = \cos\theta\, d\theta \tag{71}$$

i.e.
$$d\theta = \sec\theta\, du . \tag{72}$$

Sec θ is generated using $d(\sec\theta) = \sec\theta\tan\theta\, d\theta$ and

$$d(\tan\theta) = \sec^2\theta\, d\theta \tag{73}$$

$$K_{z_{10}} = K_{y_1} = K_{y_4} = K_{y_7} . \tag{74}$$

If the scale constant on du is K and the maximum allowable value of $\sec\theta$ is M and of $\tan\theta$ is M_{10} from equation (13):

$$K_{z_1} = MK = K_{x_4} \tag{75}$$

$$K_{z_4} = M^2 K = K_{x_{10}} = K_{x_7} \tag{76}$$

$$K_{z_7} = M^3 K = K_{y_{10}} \tag{77}$$

$$K_{z_{10}} = M^2 M_{10} K = K_{y_1} = K_{y_4} = K_{y_7} . \tag{78}$$

Applying equation (10):

$$K_{z_{10}} = N_{10} K_{x_{10}} K_{y_{10}} \tag{79}$$

$$M_{10} M^2 K = N_{10} M^2 K \cdot M^3 K \tag{80}$$

i.e.
$$N_{10} = \frac{M_{10}}{M^3 K} . \tag{81}$$

Similarly by applying equation (12) it can be seen that:

$$N = \frac{M}{M^2 M_{10} K}$$

i.e.
$$N = \frac{1}{M M_{10} K}$$

for each of the other integrators.

An arrangement of integrators to form a cosec $\theta - \cot \theta$ loop to obtain the inverse of cos θ is shown in Figure 3.14.

If
$$u = \cos \theta \qquad (82)$$

$$du = \sin \theta \, d\theta \qquad (83)$$

i.e.
$$d\theta = -\cosec \theta \, du \qquad (83)$$

i.e. $d(\cosec \theta) = -\cot \theta \cosec \theta \, d\theta, \quad d(\cot \theta) = -\cosec^2 \theta \, d\theta .$ (85)

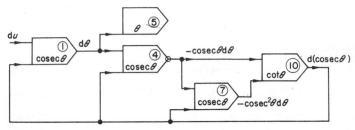

Figure 3.14. *Inverse cosine.*

3.6 Adders

In all the diagrams previously described, the integrator ΔX inputs were provided either by the machine source or by the output of one integrator. In more complex programs, an integrator ΔX input may be the sum of the output of two or more integrators. As described in Chapter 2 the ΔX and ΔY inputs of an integrator perform fundamentally different functions. The ΔY increments provide numerical data for the Y number and therefore two or more can be accepted in the same iteration period. The ΔX increments control the addition or subtraction of the Y number and the R number and so only one increment can be accepted per iteration period. Thus when the ΔX increments are provided by two or more sources they must be accumulated, stored and presented to the integrator one per iteration period. The unit carrying out this task may conveniently be termed an adder. As discussed in Chapters 1, 2 and 7 it is possible to provide every integrator of a d.d.a. with this facility but this requires a large amount of logic. Some d.d.a.'s have specialized adder units as well as integrators. It is, however, possible with most d.d.a.'s to program integrators as adders, as is now described.

3.6.1 *The hard adder*

Consider an integrator programmed as shown in Figure 3.15 with the ΔX input from machine time ΔT and a ΔY input from the ΔZ output. Let the initial Y number be $-N$, a full register. During the first iteration, the output will be -1 increment. For the second iteration, the Y number will become

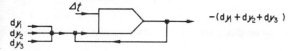

$$-(dy_1 + dy_2 + dy_3)$$

Figure 3.15. *Hard adder.*

$(-N-1) \equiv N-1$ and the output $+1$ increment. For the third iteration the Y number becomes $+N \equiv -N$. The output of this integrator is thus -1, $+1$, -1, $+1$, etc., i.e. zero rate and the Y number retains dynamic stability about the $-N$ state. If the integrator had received an additional ΔY increment of $+1$ at the second iteration, the Y number would have become $-N$, and an output of -1 increment resulted. During the third iteration, the Y number would become $N-1$, and the output $+1$. In this case, the output was -1 -1 $+1$ -1 etc., a net output of -1. Similarly with an additional -1 input increment, a net $+1$ output occurs. The integrator may have several additional ΔY inputs, dy_1, dy_2, dy_3, etc. producing the output $-(dy_1 + dy_2 + dy_3)$.

A single integrator programmed in this way introduces an error. The number $-N$ differs in magnitude from the number $N-1$ by one increment. Thus with no additional ΔY inputs the integrator has a net output of -1 increment every N iterations. This error can be removed by passing the output of the adder through a second adder as shown in Figure 3.16. The -1 increment

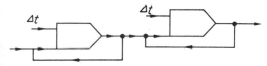

Figure 3.16. *Hard adders in series.*

produced by the first adder becomes a $+1$ increment on passing through the second adder thus cancelling the -1 increment produced by the second adder.

Integrators employing binary or ternary transfer can be programmed as described above. However, it can be seen that for an integrator employing ternary transfers the output is effectively binary thus introducing binary drift

errors in subsequent integrators. This difficulty can be avoided if the logic
of the ternary integrators is such that the output is inhibited when the Y
number is $-N$. The adder will not then give an output until an input increment is passed to it. If the increment is $+1$ the Y number becomes $-N+1$,
the output is -1, and on the next iteration the Y number reverts to $-N$.
Similarly if the increment is -1, the Y number becomes $N-1$, the output
is $+1$ and on the next iteration the Y number reverts to $-N$. An adder of this
type will not produce an output error. The condition when the output of an
integrator is inhibited with a Y number of $-N$ will be termed the stall condition and an integrator with its output inhibited in this way will be said to
be stalled.

A necessary condition for the operation of a hard adder is that the net
input rate should not exceed one increment per iteration. If the rate is greater
than this, increments will accumulate in the Y register of the adder causing
reduction of the output rate and eventually leading to logical failure of the
adder. In order that temporary excessive input rates shall not seriously affect
the performance of the adder, it is usual to employ the maximum available
register capacity. The stall condition with maximum register capacity will
be termed for convenience ∞.

3.6.2 *The soft adder*

An integrator programmed as shown in Figure 3.17 with an initial Y number
of zero, functions as a soft adder. As dy_1, dy_2, dy_3, etc. increments are passed
to the integrator, the Y number and hence the rate of production of ΔZ

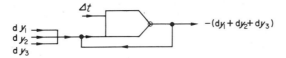

Figure 3.17. *Soft adder.*

output increments increases. The sign change produces ΔZ output increments
of opposite sign to the $dy_1 + dy_2 + dy_3$, input. The Y number therefore increases until the ΔZ output increment rate is equal to the input rate. The
output rate will thereafter remain approximately equal to the input rate.

The response of a soft adder to changes of input rate is dependent on the
register length used. A short register length gives a rapid response. The input
rate must not exceed one increment per iteration for long periods, as the

Y number will then try to exceed the register capacity, i.e. will overflow. A logical failure then occurs.

Soft adders are useful for smoothing out high frequency oscillations of an input rate derived from an external source.

3.7 Servo techniques

Most functions required for d.d.a. computations can be computed analytically. However, in some cases convenient analytical methods cannot be found and servo techniques must be used. An incremental error signal is produced which triggers a source of increments of the unknown function correcting this function until the error is eliminated.

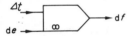

Figure 3.18. *Servo active element.*

The active element which provides increments of the function can conveniently be produced in a ternary d.d.a. with stall facility by an initially stalled integrator with a ΔX input from machine time and a ΔY input from the error source (Figure 3.18). The output, df, is of opposite sign to the error e. Alternatively the active element can be produced by connecting two adders to form a closed loop (Figure 3.19). Any error increment passed to the input

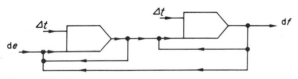

Figure 3.19. *Servo active element.*

of the first adder will circulate continuously through both adders until an increment of opposite sign is introduced. The output of the second adder is of the same sign as the error signal.

The flow diagrams of the following examples are drawn for convenience for a ternary d.d.a. with stall facility.

3.7.1 *The square root*

Let
$$x = \sqrt{Y}. \tag{86}$$

Increments dy of y will be available

$$x^2 = y \qquad (87)$$

$$-2x\,dx + dy = 0. \qquad (88)$$

In the flow diagram given in Figure 3.20 an input ΔY increment of $+1$ will unstall integrator (1). The sign change produces positive output dx increments

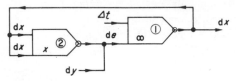

Figure 3.20. *Square root servo.*

which increase x until (2) gives a negative output to stall (1). Similarly with a negative dy increment x is decreased. This computation will be inaccurate when y is near zero as a change of one increment in y then requires a change of many increments in x to balance the servo.

3.7.2 *Inverse tangent*
Assuming increments d$(\tan \theta)$ are available, it is possible to compute dθ by a servo method:

$$d(\tan \theta) = -\sec^2 \theta\, d\theta \qquad (89)$$

$$d(\sec \theta) = \sec \theta \tan \theta\, d\theta. \qquad (90)$$

The above two equations are utilized to compute d$(\tan \theta)$ using incre-

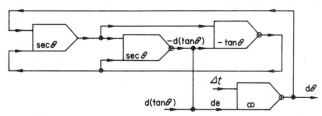

Figure 3.21. *Inverse tangent servo.*

ments derived from the servo active element shown in Figure 3.21. The active element is triggered by the difference between the input d$(\tan \theta)$ and the computated d$(\tan \theta)$.

The program cannot be scaled when $\theta \to (2n-1)\frac{1}{2}\pi$ as $\tan \theta$ and $\sec \theta \to \infty$.

3.7.3 *Differential equations*

It is not usually necessary to resort to servo methods to solve differential equations. Servo methods can be applied as demonstrated below. The equation:

$$t \frac{dy}{dt} + y = 0 \tag{91}$$

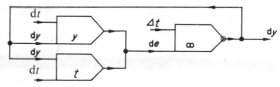

Figure 3.22. Differential equation servo.

can be solved as shown in Figure 3.22, if increments dt of t are available. The servo equation is:

$$t\,dy + y\,dt = 0. \tag{92}$$

3.7.4 *Differentiation*

Differentiation cannot be carried out satisfactorily on the d.d.a. A servo method is possible:

$$dy - \frac{dy}{dx}\,dx = 0. \tag{93}$$

The flow diagram is shown in Figure 3.23. As the Y number of integrator (1) can change by many increments without affecting greatly the output rate

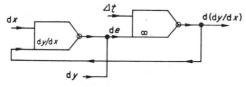

Figure 3.23. Servo differentiation.

of (2), the value of dy/dx tends to oscillate. These oscillations may build up to an amplitude which causes overflow of the register.

A fair approximation to a derivative is obtained by a soft adder. Since the output rate is approximately equal to the input rate, the Y number is an

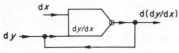

Figure 3.24. *Servo differentiation.*

approximation to the derivative of the adder input with respect to the ΔX input. The sum of the ΔY inputs gives the increments of the derivative (Figure 3.24). The value of derivative computed in this way lags the correct value.

3.7.5 *Stability*

Like most servo systems d.d.a. servo programs can become unstable or inaccurate in certain circumstances. Care should be taken that the program is scaled so that an error increment is removed as a result of a small number of increments provided by the output of the active element. If this condition is not met, the results will be inaccurate and also the servo might break down at the scaling limits as a result of the errors.

The servo active element should provide ΔX inputs to integrators whose outputs dominate the error signal. If ΔY inputs only are provided, oscillations can develop in the computed quantities. One disadvantage of servo methods is that the computed function changes in steps at full machine rate. This may cause difficulties in further parts of a computation. In general, servo methods should be avoided wherever possible.

3.8 Amble's method

This technique is valuable for computing certain functions which would otherwise either require the use of servo methods or utilize an excessive number of integrators. It was developed by Amble for use with the Bush mechanical differential analyser.

Let u and v be functions of an unknown x which can be computed by conventional d.d.a. methods. They are related by the equation:

$$\mathrm{d}u = v\,\mathrm{d}x \,. \tag{94}$$

Then since $\mathrm{d}u$ and $\mathrm{d}v$ are available x can be computed from:

$$(v-1)\mathrm{d}x - \mathrm{d}u = -\mathrm{d}x \,. \tag{95}$$

The flow diagram is shown in Figure 3.25. The scaling of this loop at first sight presents difficulties since:

$$M_{v-1} K_x = K_x \tag{96}$$

i.e. $$M_{v-1} = 1 \tag{97}$$

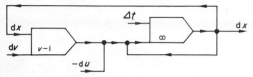

Figure 3.25. *Amble's method.*

and hence $0 \leqslant v \leqslant 2$ thus apparently imposing an unacceptable limitation on v. However the equation can be re-written as:

$$(Sv-1)dx - S du = -dx \tag{98}$$

where S is an arbitrary constant. Here $0 \leqslant Sv \leqslant 2$ and if $S \leqslant 2/v$ the program is valid for all positive values of v and only valid if v does not change sign. If v is negative the equation is re-written as:

$$-(1+Sv)dx + S du = -dx \tag{99}$$

where

$$-2 \leqslant Sv \leqslant 0. \tag{100}$$

The results of the computation become inaccurate when Sv approaches zero since $Sv-1$ approaches a full register and each input increment of $S du$ will cause many dx increments to circulate through the adder and the integrator holding $Sv-1$. Also if the $S du$ input is not small the input to the adder can exceed full machine rate in these circumstances. The main advantage of Amble's method over servo methods is that the dx rate varies smoothly. It is illustrated by the following examples:

3.8.1 *Square root*

$$u = x^2 \tag{101}$$

$$du - 2x dx \tag{102}$$

$$(2x-1)dx - du = -dx. \tag{103}$$

The flow diagram is given in Figure 3.26. In common with all other square root programs this becomes inaccurate as u approaches zero.

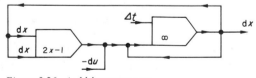

Figure 3.26. *Amble's square root.*

3.8.2 *Quotient*

Let
$$x = u/v \tag{104}$$

$$xv = u \tag{105}$$

$$x\,dv + v\,dx = du \tag{106}$$

$$(v-1)dx - du + x\,dv = -dx . \tag{107}$$

The flow diagram is shown in Figure 3.27. This is one of the most useful of the Amble programs.

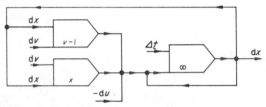

Figure 3.27. *Amble quotient.*

3.8.3 *Arc sin and arc cosine*

$$d(\sin \theta) = \cos \theta\, d\theta \tag{108}$$

$$(\cos \theta - 1)d\theta - d(\sin \theta) = -d\theta . \tag{109}$$

The flow diagram is given in Figure 3.28. Similarly:

$$(\sin \theta - 1)d\theta + d(\cos \theta) = d\theta . \tag{110}$$

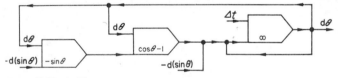

Figure 3.28. *Amble arc sin.*

3.9 The integrator as a decision unit

In many d.d.a. programs it may prove necessary or desirable to place some controls on the computation. Most control operations involve switching on or off the independent variable input to parts of the computation. The independent variable inputs can be controlled by integrators programmed as shown in Figures 3.18 and 3.19 but with ΔX inputs from the independent variable instead of machine time. Switching is accomplished in both cases by a single 'de' increment which must be provided at a precise moment in the computation.

The following descriptions are given in terms of a typical d.d.a. employing ternary transfer and the stall facility, but analogous reasoning will lead to similar programs for other d.d.a.'s.

Consider an integrator with a capacity N containing a constant Y number of 1 increment and an initial R number R_0. If the ΔX input is positive and the Y increment is positive, or if the ΔX input is negative and the Y increment negative, then with successive ΔX inputs the register will count positively in the sequence $R_0+1, R_0+2, R_0+3, \ldots N-2, N-1, 0, 1, 2$, etc. When the R number changes from $N-1$ to 0 a positive ΔZ output increment occurs. This is after $N-R_0$ increments have been passed to the ΔX input. If the ΔX input and Y increment are of opposite sign the R register will count negatively in the sequence $R_0-1, R_0-2, \ldots 2, 1, 0, N-1$ etc.

When the R number changes from 0 to $N-1$, a negative ΔZ output increment occurs. This is after a net R_0+1 increments have been passed to the ΔX input. Thus by setting R_0 it is possible accurately to time any event in a computation. The integrator output increment can be used to stall or unstall an integrator. This process forms the basis of all program control.

In some cases it may not prove convenient to pre-set an R number other than zero. A constant comprised of C increments can be used in the Y register when a positive count will give an output increment after N/C input increments. This method is not so accurate due to rounding of N/C. The following examples of program controls assume that unless otherwise stated the initial R number in all the integrators of the flow diagrams is zero.

3.9.1 *The switch*

The switch is one of the most commonly used program controls. It emits a fixed number of increments and then gives no further output thus switching

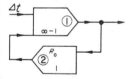

Figure 3.29. *The switch.*

off a computation. The flow diagram is shown in Figure 3.29. Assume ∞ represents a register capacity of 10,000, $\infty-1$ is therefore $+9,999$. Integrator (1) has ΔX input from machine time. During the first iteration (1) will give no output, but for the next 9,999 will have an output of full machine rate. After $10,000 - R_0$ increments have been emitted from (1), (2) will give a positive output increment to stall (1). If more than 10,000 increments are required a third integrator may be included between (1) and (2) to scale down the input to (2). Alternative initial conditions are $\infty + 1$ in the Y register of (1) when sign changes are necessary on the outputs of (1) and (2).

Some programs are composed of several phases each with a distinct in-

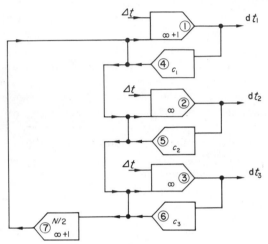

Figure 3.30. *Three-phase switch.*

dependent variable input. The control may be accomplished by a multiple switch. Figure 3.30 shows a three-phase switch at the start of a computation. (1, 2, 3) have ΔX inputs from machine time, and their outputs dt_1, dt_2, dt_3, from the independent variable inputs to the phases 1, 2, 3 of a computation. (4, 5, 6) each with capacity N, hold C_1, C_2, C_3, increments respectively. The switch operates as follows:

(1) emits N/C_1 increments and is then stalled. The increments which stalls (1) changes (2) to the $\infty - 1$ state. (2) now emits N/C_2 increments and is then stalled. The increment which stalls (2) changes (3) to $\infty + 1$. (3) now emits N/C_3 increments and is then stalled. The negative increment which stalls (3) has its sign changed by (7) which has $\infty + 1$ in its Y register, and a half full

R register, thus giving an output increment immediately on receipt of a ΔX increment. The output returns (1) to its initial $\infty + 1$ state allowing the sequence of operations to be repeated. In the case of a multiple switch with an even number of phases the sign change integrator would be unnecessary as the increment which stalled the last stage would be of correct sign to unstall the first stage.

3.9.2 *The limit switch*

In some programs it is necessary to switch off the incremental input of a variable when the variable reaches a limiting value and switch on again if the variable subsequently falls below this value. This can be accomplished by three integrators programmed as shown in Figure 3.31. dx is the incremental input subject to control. It is passed to the program via (1) which has an initial R number large enough to ensure that an output can be given for each dx input. (2) of capacity N also has a ΔX input dx and has $+1$ increment in the Y register. Suppose x has an initial value x_0 and must be switched off when it reaches x_1. If (2) has an initial R number R_0 where $R_0 = N - (x_1 - x_0)$ it will emit one positive increment when x becomes x_1 and stall (1). If x subsequently becomes less than x_1, (2) will emit a negative increment and

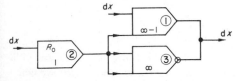

Figure 3.31. *The limit switch.*

unstall (1). The input to (2) should be scaled so that x cannot exceed x_1 by more than $N - 1$ increments otherwise a further spurious increment could be emitted falsely to unstall (1).

(1) will not give an output for the dx increment initiating the stall, but will give an output for the dx input causing the unstall. Thus the output of (1) will drift by one increment for every on/off switching sequence. This drift is corrected by (3) which has ΔX and ΔY inputs from (2) and is initially stalled. The input of a positive increment will unstall (3) which will give an output increment made positive by the sign change facility. The subsequent input of a negative increment will stall (3) which will not give an output. Thus the sum of the output of (2, 3) will provide the required controlled variable dx.

3.9.3 *Rate control*

One application of the limit switch is the control of the rate of a computation. Many programs incorporate a hard adder as an essential part. When this adder has a large number of inputs the sum of these inputs may be greater than full machine rate during part of the computation and increments will accumulate in the Y register of the adder. In general, this difficulty can be avoided by careful scaling but this may lead to an excessive computation time. Alternatively the input of machine time to the independent variable inputs of the computation can be reduced thus temporarily reducing the rate of solution of the problem. Figure 3.32 shows the required flow diagram.

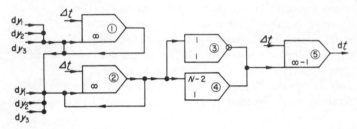

Figure 3.32. *Rate control.*

(1) is an adder with inputs dy_1, dy_2, dy_3, which may together exceed full machine rate. These three inputs together with the output of (1) are summed in a second adder (2). The output of (2) will only exceed ± 1 increment if $(dy_1 + dy_2 + dy_3)$ exceeds machine rate. (3, 4) form two limit switches which operate when the output of (2) reaches ± 2 increments. The limit switches stall (5) which has a ΔX input from machine time and an output dt which forms the independent variable input to the computation of dy_1, dy_2, dy_3. (3,4) both have a single increment in their Y registers. (3) has a sign change and a single increment in the R register. It will therefore emit a positive increment when the output of (2) reaches -2 increments. (4) has $N-2$ increments in the R register and will therefore emit a positive increment when the output of (2) reaches $+2$ increments.

When dt is switched off, (1) will continue to emit output increments until the accumulated increments in the Y register falls below ± 2, when dt will be switched on again. The net result is a reduced independent variable input rate to the computation. This procedure may also be applied to the accumulation of error increments in the Y register of an integrator forming the active element of a servo to stabilize the servo.

3.10 The integrator as a store

Although the d.d.a. is essentially an incremental computer it is desirable in some programs to store and transfer whole numbers. For example a constant may require changing part way through a computation. If the d.d.a. has an associated general-purpose digital computer, as described in Chapter 8, this operation can readily be accomplished, but with a simple d.d.a. integrators must be used.

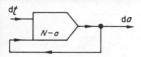

Figure 3.33. Storage integrator.

Storage and transfer can be accomplished by an integrator programmed as shown in Figure 3.33. When dt increments are passed to the ΔX input the integrator will emit $+a$ increments and then stop. If the ΔX input comes from a switch the timing of this transfer can be controlled.

During transfer the integrator is performing in an identical manner to the computation of e^t (see Section 3.5.1). The minimum number of the increments necessary to change the Y number from $N-a$ to N, i.e. clear the store, can therefore readily be calculated. It has been shown in Section 3.5.1 that the scale constant of the ΔX input to an exponential computation is $1/N$ while the scale constant of the ΔY input can be freely selected by the programmer. In this case let it be $1/N$ making $M=1$. Thus a full register represents a value or e^t of 1, i.e. $t=0$.

The initial value of t is given by:

$$N^{-1}(N-a) = e^t \tag{111}$$

$$t = \log_e [1 - (a/N)] . \tag{112}$$

Thus the number of increments to clear the store, i.e. increase t to zero is:

$$-N \log_e [1 - (a/N)] . \tag{113}$$

The following example will describe storage systems employing a ternary d.d.a. with stall facility.

3.10.1 *Linear interpolation*

Integrators programmed as stores can be used to give a linear interpolation between successive results of a computation. In this example the interpolation takes place in four phases controlled by the outputs dt_1, dt_2, dt_3, and

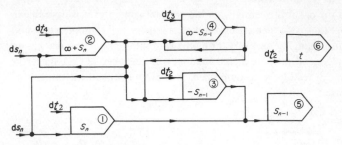

Figure 3.34. *Linear interpolation.*

dt_4, of a four-phase switch. Figure 3.34 shows the flow diagram with conditions at the start of phase 2.

During phase 1 the current result S_n has been computed and is held in the Y register of integrator (1) and storage integrator (2). The previous result of the computation S_{n-1} is stored as $-S_{n-1}$ in (3, 4). During phase 2 the sum of the outputs of (1, 3) will be a linear interpolation between S_{n-1} and S_n. It is accumulated in (5) and can be plotted against time held in (6). In phase 3 (4) will emit S_{n-1} changing the Y register of (3) to zero, and of (4) to ∞. In phase 4 (2) will emit $-S_n$ to clear (1, 2) to zero and ∞ and pass $-S_n$ to (3, 4). The system is then ready for the next stage of the interpolation.

3.10.2 *Arbitrary function generation*

It is sometimes necessary to generate functions in the d.d.a. which result from experimental data and cannot conveniently be simulated by a single straight line, sine wave, parabola etc. It is possible, using storage integrators, to simulate the analogue computer method of generating arbitrary functions by fitting a set of straight lines to the function as shown in Figure 3.35.

The flow diagram for generating the approximation to an arbitrary function by nine straight lines, shown in Figure 3.36, gives the conditions at the start of the computation which is controlled by a three-phase switch with outputs dt_1, dt_2, dt_3. In general the phases will be of equal length. In phase 1 the approximation is given by the output of (4). During the first phase 1,

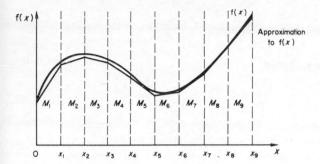

Figure 3.35. *Approximation to an arbitrary function.*

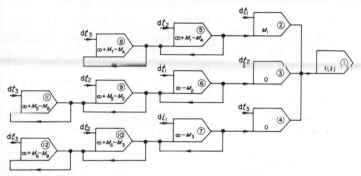

Figure 3.36. *Arbitrary function generator.*

(2) holds M_1 the slope of the first line of the approximation. The approximation is $M_1 . dt_1$.

During phase 1, the contents of stores (6, 7) are passed to (3, 4) which at the end of the first phase 1 will hold M_2 and M_3. During phase 2 the contents of stores (5, 9, 10) are passed to (2, 6, 7) which at the end of the first phase 2 will hold M_4, $-(M_5 - M_2)$, and $-(M_6 - M_3)$. This transfer process continues until the end of the third phase 2 when (2, 3, 4) will hold M_4, M_8, M_9. Operations of the third phase 3 will complete the approximation.

4: Error Analysis

4.1 Introduction

On examination of the basic integration process described in Chapter 2 it is clear that digital integration can never be exact. All digital quantities are discrete both in amplitude and time and can never represent continuous variables exactly. The process can be made as accurate as required by making the step size sufficiently small or the solution rate sufficiently large, but it will never be completely accurate. Thus two kinds of error will arise in any digital integration process which, for convenience, will be referred to as 'round-off' and 'truncation' respectively. Round-off occurs because the digital quantity can only change in discrete steps and truncation occurs because the quantity only changes at discrete intervals of time.

In the case of the simple rectangular integration process which is used in the conventional d.d.a. the main manifestation of the truncation effect is an inability to retrace calculations exactly. For instance, in using the d.d.a. to generate a function it is found that, starting from a given initial condition, an increase in the independent variable followed by an equal decrease results in a small residual change in the value of the function. In other words, one does not get back to the value from which one started. As a result, it is possible to get progressive drifts in the values of functions for oscillatory inputs. Round-off effects can also cause drift but these are usually of a smaller order of magnitude.

There are two ways in which it is possible to approach the matter of d.d.a. errors, viz.: the arithmetic or the analytic. It is possible by purely arithmetic considerations to deduce the existence of integrator drift for simple schematics and also to obtain a measure of its order of magnitude. The analytic method, which is based on the calculus of finite differences, is much to be preferred, however, since, in addition to giving the magnitude of the drift errors, it also shows what are the underlying causes of these errors. In this chapter the analytic method is used throughout.

While it is possible to make an analysis for a general integrator schematic, this is complex and does not reveal the fundamental causes of d.d.a. errors.

58

It is difficult to make overall statements about errors other than those which have been made already, rather it has been found more useful to consider particular functions on their individual merits, an approach adopted in this chapter.

While the method to be described is perfectly general, it is proposed, in order to keep the mathematics within reasonable bounds of complexity to consider the following particular functions:

- (a) simple integration
- (b) multiplication by a constant
- (c) the squarer
- (d) the exponential function
- (e) sin and cosine.

The first function stands apart from the rest but it is of the greatest importance and forms an illuminating example of the application of the theory.

Most of the analysis will be formulated in terms of ternary transfer between integrators, but the sin/cosine equations will also be set up in terms of binary transfer to see what effect this has on the integrator errors. Another aspect which will be covered in this chapter will be the effect of the difference between sequential and simultaneous operation of d.d.a.'s.

4.2 Simple integration

Broadly speaking, d.d.a. integrators may be used for two purposes, namely, simple integration and function generation. For simple integration the independent variable proceeds by equal steps and usually this means that the device is integrating with respect to time. It is only when one requires function generation that it is necessary to make use of the facility of integration with respect to an arbitrary variable.

In the example to be considered the errors which arise in the integration of an analogue function with respect to time are derived. It is first necessary to convert the function into digital form by means of a digitizer, and the digital number is inserted into the Y register of an integrator whose X input is time. The overflows resulting from the first integrator are accumulated in the Y register of a second integrator and this number represents the value of the integral. The arrangement is shown in Figure 4.1 where the increments or overflows are represented by δZ and the number accumulated in the second integrator is Z.

The first error to be considered is the effect of the conversion from analogue to digital representation of a function. Figure 4.2 shows a typical analogue

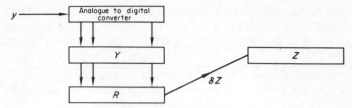

Figure 4.1. *Simple integration of an analogue function.*

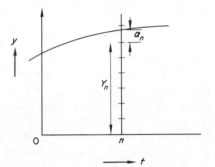

Figure 4.2. *Round off effect of digital converter.*

function as a smooth curve which takes the value y_n at the end of the nth integration step. Because of the finite step size of the converter the digital number which emerges is Y_n which differs from the input by α_n the round-off. This effect may be represented by the equation:

$$Y_n = y_n - \alpha_n . \tag{1}$$

To deal with the integration process it is necessary to introduce more notation. Supposing that n steps of integration have occurred then, at the beginning of the $(n+1)$th step the converter is sampled and its output Y_n is inserted into the Y register of the first integrator. Y_n is then added to R_n, the number in the R register, and causes it to change to R_{n+1}. An overflow δZ_n is then generated which is added to the integrand of the second integrator and changes its contents from Z_n to Z_{n+1}.

Thus: $$Z_{n+1} = Z_n + \delta Z_n . \tag{2}$$

In order to obtain the relation between the overflow δZ and the Y/R numbers in the first integrator it is necessary to define the capacity of the R register. This is taken as M units, by which is meant that if M units are added into the R register an overflow of one unit is produced. When Y_n is added into the R register three possibilities may occur:

(i) zero overflow, in which case:

$$\delta Z_n = 0 \text{ and } R_{n+1} = R_n + Y_n \tag{3}$$

(ii) positive overflow, in which case:

$$\delta Z_n = 1 \text{ and } R_{n+1} = R_n + Y_n - M \tag{4}$$

(iii) negative overflow, in which case:

$$\delta Z_n = -1 \text{ and } R_{n+1} = R_n + Y_n + M . \tag{5}$$

These three results may be combined into one formula as:

$$\delta Z_n = \frac{1}{M}(Y_n + R_n - R_{n+1}) . \tag{6}$$

Summing this equation from $n=0$ to $n=N-1$ where N is the total number of steps gives:

$$Z_n - Z_0 = \frac{1}{M}(Y_0 + Y_1 + \ldots + Y_{N-1}) + \frac{1}{M}(R_0 - R_N) \tag{7}$$

and this is the mathematical form of the result of performing N steps of digital integration.

This equation may be written in the form:

$$Z_n + \frac{R_N}{M} = \frac{1}{M}(R_0 + Y_0 + Y_1 + \ldots + Y_{N-1}) \tag{8}$$

in which one can regard Z_n and R_N/M as the most and least significant halves respectively of a digital number. Starting with R_0 in the least significant half, the integration process may be regarded as the successive addition of the numbers $Y_0, Y_1, \ldots Y_{N-1}$ into the least significant half of the double length number. The integration process is thus seen to be a matter of summation of rectangles as shown in Figure 4.3.

Introducing the round-off effect into equation (7) by the use of equation (1) gives:

$$Z_n - Z_0 = \frac{1}{M}(y_0 + y_1 + \ldots + y_{N-1}) + \frac{1}{M}(R_0 - R_N) - \frac{1}{M}(\alpha_0 + \alpha_1 + \ldots + \alpha_{N-1}) . \tag{9}$$

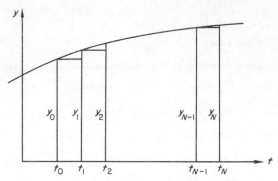

Figure 4.3. *Integration as summation of rectangles.*

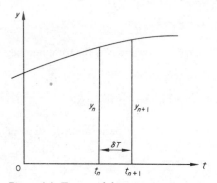

Figure 4.4. *Trapezoidal integration.*

The final step is to relate the quantity $y_0 + y_1 + \ldots + Y_{N-1}$ to the area under the curve. A sufficient approximation to give the error may be obtained by the use of trapezoidal integration. Suppose that the integration steps occur at the times $t_0, t_1, \ldots t_{N-1}$ in which the time interval between successive steps is equal to δT, then the area under the curve lying between t_n and t_{n+1} is shown in Figure 4.4 and is equal to:

$$\tfrac{1}{2}\delta T(y_n + y_{n+1}).$$

Thus:

$$\int_{t_0}^{t_N} y \cdot dt = \tfrac{1}{2}\delta T(y_0 + y_1) + \tfrac{1}{2}\delta T(y_1 + y_2) + \ldots + \tfrac{1}{2}(y_{N-1} + y_N)$$

$$= \tfrac{1}{2}\delta T(y_N - y_0) + \delta T(y_0 + y_1 + \ldots + y_{N-1}). \tag{10}$$

Substituting from this into equation (9) gives:

$$Z_N - Z_0 = \frac{1}{M \delta T} \int_{t_0}^{t_N} y \, . \, dt \; - \; \frac{1}{2M} (y_N - y_0) \; + \; \frac{1}{M} (R_0 - R_N) +$$
$$- \; \frac{1}{M} (\alpha_0 + \alpha_1 + \ldots + \alpha_{N-1}). \tag{11}$$

Equation (11) gives the value of the number in the Z register in terms of the area under the curve and shows the various errors involved. The first point to note is that the scale factor $(M \delta T)^{-1}$ has been introduced. This has the effect of making the equation non-dimensional, Z_N being a pure number in fact. There are three error terms which will now be discussed in turn.

The term $(y_N - y_0)/2M$ is due to the sampling of the curve at discrete instants of time and is the truncation error mentioned in the introduction. This term does not represent the complete truncation error but it is the most significant component. It is, in fact, the contribution arising from the $(\delta T)^2$ term in the Taylor expansion of the integral. To obtain an idea of its likely order of magnitude we note that, since the capacity of the Y register is M units, y can never exceed M units in magnitude for a correctly scaled problem. Thus in the worst possible case y_N is $+M$ and y_0 is $-M$, or vice versa, and the magnitude of this term is one unit or quantum. Thus for simple integration the truncation error will never exceed one unit in the Y register.

The term $(R_0 - R_N)/M$ is the first rounding error and it arises from the number in the R register of the first integrator. Recalling the remarks made concerning equation (8) it may be seen that this effect arises because one is rounding off the least significant half of a double length number. Since the R number can only vary between 0 and M the greatest value which this error may take is one unit. If R_0 is made equal to $M/2$ this error never exceeds half a unit.

The term $(\alpha_0 + \alpha_1 + \ldots + \alpha_{N-1})/M$ is due to the rounding effect of the analogue to digital converter and it differs from the previous error in that it depends on the number of integration steps taken. This is most conveniently represented as an error rate. Since the average value of the α's is clearly half a unit this term contributes error at the rate of one-half a unit in M integration steps.

Ignoring the rounding effect of the digizer it can be seen that the truncation and rounding effects in the purely digital process of integration have the same order of magnitude, viz.: about one unit of least significance in the integral. In this sense it is true to say that in the simple integration process as exemplified by the d.d.a. integrator, the rounding and truncation effects are balanced and any attempt to improve one effect must be accompanied by a corresponding improvement in the other.

4.3 Multiplication by a constant

The usual way of multiplying a variable quantity by a constant is to put the constant into the integrand of an integrator whose independent variable input is the increments of the variable according to the incremental equation:

$$\delta Z = K \delta X \tag{12}$$

where K is the constant quantity.

If δX_n is the independent variable increment in the nth step, K must be multiplied by δX_n before being added into the R register. The expression for the output overflow now becomes:

$$\delta Z_n = \frac{1}{M}(K\delta X_n + R_n - R_{n+1}) = Z_{n+1} - Z_n. \tag{13}$$

If the overflows are accumulated in the integrand of another integrator to form a number Z, this may be obtained by summing equation (13) from $n=0$ to $n=N-1$:

$$Z_N - Z_0 = \frac{1}{M}K(X_N - X_0) - \frac{1}{M}(R_N - R_0). \tag{14}$$

This expression shows that the only error which occurs in this operation is due to the remainder term in the R register and in the worst case it can only amount to one unit in the Z number. If R_0 is made equal to $M/2$ the maximum error is reduced to half a unit.

Writing equation (13) in the form:

$$Z_{n+1} + \frac{1}{M} \cdot R_{n+1} = Z_n + \frac{1}{M} \cdot R_n + \frac{1}{M} \cdot K \cdot \delta X_n \tag{15}$$

it becomes obvious that multiplication by a constant merely consists of multiplying K by δX and adding it into the bottom half of a double length register. A further point which may be noted is that the error is limited to one unit regardless of the behaviour of the variable quantity X and no systematic drift occurs in this operation.

4.4 The squarer

The d.d.a. schematic for calculating the square of a function is shown in Figure 4.5 in which the δX quantity is fed to both the independent variable input and to the integrand. The corresponding incremental equation is:

$$\tfrac{1}{2}\delta(X^2) = X\delta X . \tag{16}$$

While it is possible to write down the full equation for a perfectly general independent variable input, this is not particularly enlightening and it is felt that important features of the behaviour can be illustrated by considering what happens when X first increases by N steps and then decreases.

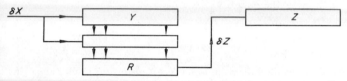

Figure 4.5. The squaring schematic

Consider first the case where X is increasing, starting with initial conditions 0, R_0 and 0 for Y, R, Z respectively. During the $(n+1)$th step Y first increases from n to $n+1$ and is then added into the R register changing its contents from R_n to R_{n+1}. An overflow δZ_n is produced which changes Z from Z_n to Z_{n+1} where δZ_n is given by the equation:

$$\delta Z_n = \frac{1}{M}(n+1+R_n-R_{n+1}) . \tag{17}$$

The effect of proceeding N steps is obtained by summing this expression from 0 to $N-1$ to give:

$$Z_N = \frac{1}{M}(1+2+ \ldots +N) + \frac{1}{M}(R_0-R_N) \tag{18}$$

$$= \frac{1}{2M} N(N+1) + \frac{1}{M}(R_0-R_N) \tag{19}$$

$$= \frac{N^2}{2M} + \frac{N}{2M} + \frac{1}{M}(R_0-R_N) . \tag{20}$$

From this expression it may be seen that the output of the squaring schematic consists of three quantities. The first term $N^2/2M$ is the correct answer and the other two which are errors. $N/2M$ is the truncation error which can amount to half a unit or quantum for a run of M steps. $(R_0 - R_N)/M$ is the rounding error which, for the worst case when $R_0 = 0$, can never exceed one unit since R_N can never be greater than $M - 1$. If R_0 is made equal to $\frac{1}{2}M$ the rounding error never exceeds half a unit.

Rewriting equation (20) in the form:

$$Z_N + \frac{1}{M} R_N = \frac{N^2}{2M} + \frac{N}{2M} + \frac{1}{M} R_0 \tag{21}$$

and remembering that both R_N and Z_N are whole or integral numbers, it may be seen that Z_N and R_N/M can be regarded as the integral and fractional parts respectively of the quantity:

$$\frac{N^2}{2M} + \frac{N}{2M} + \frac{1}{M} R_0 .$$

It can now be seen that the round-off effect is merely the result of ignoring the fractional part of the above expression. The effect of the truncation term $N/2M$ is to build up gradually in the R register and cause overflows to be transmitted to the Z number at a rate slightly exceeding the correct value.

To investigate possible drift effects a further run of N steps with X decreasing from N to 0 must be considered. An important thing to realize at this stage is that, although X is decreasing, the order of the operations in the integration process for the conventional d.d.a. is unchanged. In other words Y is decreased by one unit before it is subtracted from the R number and not after.

Keeping this in mind, the change in Z for N steps backwards is seen to be:

$$Z_{2N} - Z_N = -\frac{1}{M}(N-1+N-2+ \dots +1+0) + \frac{1}{M}(R_N - R_{2N})$$

$$= -\frac{N^2}{2M} + \frac{N}{2M} + \frac{1}{M}(R_N - R_{2N}) . \tag{22}$$

Adding equations (20) and (22) the net result of N steps forward followed by N steps backward is given by:

$$Z_{2N} = \frac{N}{M} + \frac{1}{M}(R_0 - R_{2N}) . \tag{23}$$

As before, regarding Z and R as the most and least significant halves of a double-length number we may write equation (23) in the form:

$$Z_{2N} + \frac{1}{M} R_{2N} = \frac{N}{M} + \frac{1}{M} R_0 . \tag{24}$$

It can be seen that the effect of the behaviour of X is to leave a remainder N/M and the calculation is not reversible. This is the first example of drift to be encountered and it is clear that it can increase indefinitely for oscillatory inputs; equation (25) shows the effect of K excursions of X:

$$Z_{2kN} + \frac{1}{M} R_{2kN} = \frac{kN}{M} + \frac{1}{M} R_0 . \tag{25}$$

While the drift remains less than one unit it is contained in the R register and does not directly affect the Z number, but successive excursions cause it to accumulate and eventually to overflow into the Z number. The rate at which the drift builds up can be obtained from equation (24) and it amounts to one unit in the Z number for a run of M steps forward followed by M steps backward.

That the truncation effect arises because of the second-order term in the independent variable increment may be seen in a general way from the following considerations. Basically one is trying to calculate the change in $\frac{1}{2}X^2$ as X increases by δX. The exact expression for this is given by:

$$\tfrac{1}{2}(X+\delta X)^2 - \tfrac{1}{2}X^2 = X . \delta X + \tfrac{1}{2}(\delta X)^2 \tag{26}$$

whereas, in the d.d.a. integrator one is calculating:

$$(X+\delta X).\delta X = X . \delta X + (\delta X)^2 . \tag{27}$$

Thus, at each step an error of $\frac{1}{2}(\delta X)^2$ is made and this is the contribution to

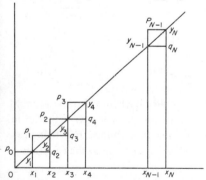

Figure 4.6. Geometrical interpretation of truncation effect.

the truncation error. To connect this up to the previous discussion it is only necessary to consider N steps and take $\delta X = 1$. Applying the scale factor $1/M$ then gives the total error $N/2M$ as before.

The geometrical interpretation of the truncation effect is illustrated in Figure 4.6 in which the line Oy_N makes an angle of $45°$ with the reference axes. The exact value of the function is given by the area under the line Oy_N. When X is increasing, however, the integrator sums the areas of the rectangles $Ox_1 y_1 p_0, x_1 x_2 y_2 p_1, \ldots x_{N-1} x_N y_N p_{N-1}$ and a small triangular error is made at each step which is equal to $\frac{1}{2}(\delta X)^2$. For decreasing X the rectangles $x_{N-1} x_N y_{N-1} q_N$ etc. are subtracted and a small error equal to the sum of the small squares $y_{N-1} q_N y_N p_{N-1}$ etc. remains. The sum of these small squares is equal to $N/2M$.

4.5 The exponential function

The schematics so far considered have been of the open loop type and it has been possible to regard the round-off effect in an elementary manner which has admitted of a simple arithmetic interpretation. For the closed loop case in which increments are fed back into the integrator schematic the round-off effect are more complex and it is proposed to illustrate this by considering the simple exponential function shown in Figure 4.7.

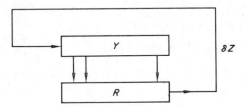

Figure 4.7. *The exponential schematic.*

The incremental equation to be solved is:

$$\delta Y = Y \delta T \tag{28}$$

implement by adding the output of the integrator back into its own integrand.

Using the same suffix notation as before, for the nth step Y has an increment added to it which increases it to Y_n and this is added to R_n to increase it to R_{n+1}. An overflow δZ_n is then produced according to the equation:

$$\delta Z_n = \frac{1}{M}\left(Y_n + R_n - R_{n+1}\right). \tag{29}$$

At the beginning of the next step the increment δZ_n is added to Y_n and changes it to Y_{n+1}. Thus the difference equation satisfied by Y_n is given by:

$$Y_{n+1} - Y_n = \frac{1}{M}(Y_n + R_n - R_{n+1}). \tag{30}$$

Substituting X_n for $Y_n + (R_n/M)$ and rearranging, the following equation is obtained:

$$X_{n+1} = \left(1 + \frac{1}{M}\right)X_n - \frac{1}{M^2}R_n. \tag{31}$$

This equation may be solved using the techniques of the calculus of finite differences but the following intuitive approach is perhaps a little clearer. Starting with initial conditions X_0 and R_0 successive solutions are seen to be:

$$X_1 = \left(1 + \frac{1}{M}\right)X_0 - \frac{1}{M^2}R_0 \tag{32}$$

$$X_2 = \left(1 + \frac{1}{M}\right)^2 X_0 - \frac{1}{M^2}\left[R_0\left(1 + \frac{1}{M}\right) + R_1\right] \tag{33}$$

$$X_3 = \left(1 + \frac{1}{M}\right)^3 X_0 - \frac{1}{M^2}\left[R_0\left(1 + \frac{1}{M}\right)^2 + R_1\left(1 + \frac{1}{M}\right) + R_2\right] \tag{34}$$

etc., and the general solution for a run of N steps is:

$$X_N = \left(1 + \frac{1}{M}\right)^N X_0 - \frac{1}{M^2}\left[R_{N-1} + R_{N-2}\left(1 + \frac{1}{M}\right) + \ldots \right.$$
$$\left. + R_0\left(1 + \frac{1}{M}\right)^{N-1}\right]. \tag{35}$$

The expression for the number in the Y register is:

$$Y_n = \left(1 + \frac{1}{M}\right)^N \left(Y_0 + \frac{1}{M}R_0\right) - \frac{1}{M}R_N - \frac{1}{M^2}\left[R_{N-1} + R_{N-2}\left(1 + \frac{1}{M}\right) + \right.$$
$$\left. \ldots + R_0\left(1 + \frac{1}{M}\right)^{N-1}\right] \tag{36}$$

Starting with an initial condition Y_0 in the Y register the correct value of the function after N steps is $Y_0 e^{N/M}$ and comparing this with the expression for Y_N, the various errors arising may be seen, namely:

(i) The function $(1 + M^{-1})^N$ is obtained instead of $e^{N/M}$. This is the truncation error. It can, however, also be regarded as a scale error on the independent variable.

(ii) Because of the initial number in the R register the coefficient of the function is $Y_0 + R_0/M$ instead of Y_0. Effectively this means that the initial condition is not determined only by Y_0 but is also affected by the initial number in the R register.

(iii) The term R_n/M which may, as before, be regarded as the effect of ignoring the fractional part of the double-length number $Y_N + R_n/M$.

(iv) The term:

$$\frac{1}{M^2}\left[R_{N-1} + R_{N-2}\left(1 + \frac{1}{M}\right) + \ldots + R_0\left(1 + \frac{1}{M}\right)^{N-1} \right]$$

which depends on the sequence of R numbers and may be regarded as a cumulative round-off effect.

From the foregoing discussion it is clear that the errors for the exponential schematic are of a more complex nature than those previous examples, in particular, rounding errors occur in three different ways.

A good approximation for examining the effect of the cumulative round-off error is to assume that all the R numbers are uniformly distributed about a mean value $M/2$ and to replace them all by this constant number. The term then becomes:

$$\frac{1}{2M}\left[1 + \left(1 + \frac{1}{M}\right) + \left(1 + \frac{1}{M}\right)^2 + \ldots + \left(1 + \frac{1}{M}\right)^{N-1} \right] =$$
$$\tfrac{1}{2}\left[\left(1 + \frac{1}{M}\right)^N - 1 \right] \qquad (37)$$

and the effect on the Y number is given by:

$$Y_N = \left(Y_0 + \frac{1}{M}R_0\right)\left(1 + \frac{1}{M}\right)^N - \tfrac{1}{2}\left[\left(1 + \frac{1}{M}\right)^N - 1\right] - \frac{1}{M}R_N$$
$$= \left(Y_0 + \frac{1}{M}R_0 - \tfrac{1}{2}\right)\left(1 + \frac{1}{M}\right)^N + \tfrac{1}{2} - \frac{1}{M}R_N. \qquad (38)$$

The cumulative round-off thus effectively reduces the initial condition by half a unit. Equation (38) also affords an explanation of the fact that the exponential schematic is more accurate if one starts with an R register which is half full. Putting $R_0 = M/2$ gives:

$$Y_N = Y_0 \left(1 + \frac{1}{M}\right)^N + \tfrac{1}{2} - \frac{1}{M} R_N \tag{39}$$

which is a much better approximation to $Y_0\, e^{N/M}$ than that given by equation (38) with $R_0 = 0$, particularly in the case where Y_0 is small.

As a check on the validity of the approximation made for the cumulative rounding error the following numerical example may be considered. Table 4.1 shows the result of a run with $M = 1000$, $Y_0 = 100$, $R_0 = 0$ in which 100 steps of the exponential d.d.a. algorithm were performed on a hand calculating machine. The corresponding values of the function given by equation (38) and of the exponential function $100\, e^{n/1000}$ were calculated.

Table 4.1

n	$Y_n + 1/1000\, R_n$	$99 \cdot 5 (1.001)^n + \tfrac{1}{2}$	$100\, e^{n/1000}$
10	101.000	100.999	
20	102.010	102.009	
30	103.030	103.029	
40	104.060	104.059	
50	105.100	105.099	105.127
60	106.151	106.150	
70	107.212	107.211	
80	108.284	108.283	
90	109.367	109.365	
100	110.461	110.459	110.517

From this table it is clear that the assumption is justified since not only does it enable one to calculate the Y number exactly, but it also gives a very good approximation to the R number. This may be seen by comparing the fractional parts of the first two functions computed in Table 4.1.

To look at drift a backward run of N steps is considered for which it is seen that the defining difference equation is:

$$X_{n+1} = X_n \left(1 - \frac{1}{M}\right) + \frac{1}{M^2} R_n. \tag{40}$$

Solving this for N steps with initial conditions X_N and R_N gives:

$$X_{2N} = X_N \left(1 - \frac{1}{M}\right)^N + \frac{1}{M^2} \left[R_{2N-1} + R_{2N-2}\left(1 - \frac{1}{M}\right) + \ldots\right.$$

$$\left. + R_N \left(1 - \frac{1}{M}\right)^{N-1}\right]. \quad (41)$$

Substituting for X_N from equation (35) gives:

$$X_{2N} = \left(1 - \frac{1}{M}\right)^N \left[X_0\left(1 + \frac{1}{M}\right)^N - \frac{1}{M^2}\left\{R_{N-1} + R_{N-2}\left(1 + \frac{1}{M}\right) + \ldots + \right.\right.$$

$$\left.\left. R_0\left(1 + \frac{1}{M}\right)^{N-1}\right\}\right] + \frac{1}{M^2}\left[R_{2N-1} + R_{2N-2}\left(1 - \frac{1}{M}\right) + \ldots + \right.$$

$$\left. R_N\left(1 - \frac{1}{M}\right)^{N-1}\right]. \quad (45)$$

Putting all the R's equal to $M/2$ and summing the resulting geometrical progressions gives:

$$X_{2N} = X_0\left(1 - \frac{1}{M^2}\right)^N + \tfrac{1}{2}\left(1 - \frac{1}{M}\right)^N\left[1 - \left(1 + \frac{1}{M}\right)^N\right] +$$

$$+ \tfrac{1}{2}\left[1 - \left(1 - \frac{1}{M}\right)^N\right]. \quad (43)$$

Simplifying and expanding the binomial terms gives:

$$X_{2N} = X_0 - \frac{N}{M^2}X_0 + \frac{N}{2M^2} \quad (44)$$

for runs in which N is small compared with M^2.

Examination of equation (44) shows the drift effect to consist of two terms, viz.: $(N/M^2)X_0$, the drift due to truncation and $N/2M^2$ due to the cumulative round-off term. Both these errors depend on the length of the run and, as before, a standard run of M steps may be considered to obtain a suitable measure of the drift rate. The truncation drift also depends on the initial condition X_0, and taking the case where $X_0 = M/2$ units a truncation drift of half a unit is obtained for an excursion of M steps. The round-off drift for M steps is clearly $1/2M$ of a unit, or, since R/N is the fractional part of X, the drift is half a unit in the R number.

4.6 The sin and cosine function

Figure 4.8 shows the d.d.a. schematic for generating the sin and cosine functions and the corresponding incremental equations are:

$$\delta(\sin \theta) = \cos \theta \, \delta\theta$$
$$\delta(\cos \theta) = -\sin \theta \, \delta\theta .$$ (45)

This is the first case in which more than one integrator is used for generating the functions to be considered and it is necessary to take account of whether the d.d.a. is operating in the sequential or simultaneous mode. This reflects itself in the basic difference equations which will now be derived for both modes of operation.

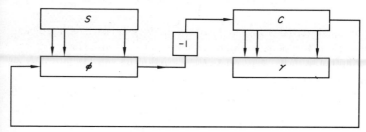

Figure 4.8. *The sin-cosine schematic.*

Let S and C be the contents of the Y registers of the integrators which produce sine and cosine respectively and let the contents of the corresponding R registers be θ and γ respectively.

Consider first the case of sequential operation and choose the notation so that the Y number in the 'cosine' integrator has just received its increment to become C_n. Let the contents of the other registers be θ_n, S_n and y_n and consider positive increments of the independent variable. In the next cycle the operations which take place are as follows:

(i) C_n is added to γ_n to change it to γ_{n+1} and an increment is produced which is added to S_n which changes it to S_{n+1} according to the equation:

$$S_{n+1} - S_n = \frac{1}{M}(\gamma_n + C_n - \gamma_{n+1}) .$$ (46)

(ii) The *new* value of S, i.e. S_{n+1} is added to θ_n to change it to θ_{n+1} and an increment is produced which, with change of sign, is added to C_n and changes it to C_{n+1} according to the equation:

$$C_{n+1} - C_n = -\frac{1}{M}(\theta_n + S_{n+1} - \theta_{n+1}). \tag{47}$$

For simultaneous operation the procedure is different in that all additions of Y to R numbers take place before increments are added to the Y numbers. Thus the cycle of operations becomes:

(i) C_n is added to γ_n to change it to γ_{n+1} and an increment is produced which changes S_n to S_{n+1} as in equation (46).

(ii) Simultaneously the old value of $S(S_n)$ is added to θ_n to produce an increment which changes C_n to C_{n+1}, and the equation corresponding to (47) becomes:

$$C_{n+1} - C_n = -\frac{1}{M}(\theta_n + S_n - \theta_{n+1}). \tag{48}$$

This seemingly trivial change in the equations does, in fact, have a profound effect on the nature of the solutions obtained and is discussed later.

Turning now to the sequential case the following substitutions may be made:

$$X_n = S_n + \frac{1}{M}\gamma_n$$

$$Y_n = C_n - \frac{1}{M}\theta_n \tag{49}$$

in the equations (46) and (47) to give:

$$X_{n+1} - X_n - \frac{1}{M}Y_n = \frac{1}{M^2}\theta_n$$

$$Y_{n+1} - Y_n + \frac{1}{M}X_{n+1} = \frac{1}{M^2}\gamma_{n+1}. \tag{50}$$

To obtain a solution to these equations it is helpful to draw a parallel to the analogous problem of the solution of simultaneous linear differential equations with forcing functions are solved by means of the particular integral and the complementary function. The particular integral is any particular solution which may be obtained by inspection or some systematic method such as the variation of parameters. The complementary functions are a set of linearly independent solutions of the homogeneous equations obtained by putting the forcing functions equal to zero. The general solution is then the sum of the particular integral and some multiple of the complementary function. Initial conditions are satisfied by adjustment of the coefficients of the complementary functions. An exactly similar approach may be taken for linear difference equations and the application to the equations (50) is now given.

The homogeneous equations to be solved are:

$$X_{n+1} - X_n - \frac{1}{M} Y_n = 0$$

$$Y_{n+1} - Y_n + \frac{1}{M} X_{n+1} = 0. \tag{51}$$

By direct substitution it may be verified that the solution to these equations is:

$$X_n = K \sin(n\alpha + \Phi)$$
$$Y_n = K \cos\left[(n+\tfrac{1}{2})\alpha + \Phi\right] \tag{52}$$

where K and Φ are arbitrary constants and $2 \sin \tfrac{1}{2}\alpha = 1/M$. If the particular integral component of the solution is $X_n = \eta_n$, $Y_d = \xi_n$ then the general solution is:

$$X_n = K \sin(n\alpha + \Phi) + \xi_n$$
$$Y_n = K \cos\left[(n+\tfrac{1}{2})\alpha + \Phi\right] + \eta_n. \tag{53}$$

The particular solution may be most conveniently obtained by the method of variation of parameters and for the sake of brevity the details are omitted here. The resulting expressions are:

$$\xi_n = \frac{1}{M^2 \cos\tfrac{1}{2}\alpha} \sum_{i=0}^{n-1} \left[\theta_i \cos(n-i-\tfrac{1}{2})\alpha - \gamma_{i+1} \sin(n-i-1)\alpha\right]$$

$$\eta_n = \frac{1}{M^2 \cos\tfrac{1}{2}\alpha} \sum_{i=0}^{n-1} \left[-\theta_i \sin(n-i)\alpha + \gamma_{i+1} \cos(n-i-\tfrac{1}{2})\alpha\right]. \tag{54}$$

Thus the general expression for the numbers in the Y registers is:

$$S_n = K \sin(n\alpha + \Phi) + \xi_n - \frac{1}{M} \gamma_n$$

$$C_n = K \cos\left[(n+\tfrac{1}{2})\alpha + \Phi\right] + \eta_n + \frac{1}{M} \theta_n. \tag{55}$$

In order to show the types of error which arise, consider a run of N steps starting from initial conditions:

$$S_0 = k \sin \varphi, \quad C_0 = k \cos \varphi.$$

Since $\xi_0 = \eta_0 = 0$, the arbitrary constants may be determined from the equations:

$$k \sin \varphi = K \sin \Phi - \frac{1}{M} \gamma_0$$

$$k \cos \varphi = K \cos(\Phi + \tfrac{1}{2}\alpha) + \frac{1}{M} \theta_0. \tag{56}$$

After N steps the solution is given by equations of the form similar to (55) with N replacing n. K and Φ may be eliminated to give the solution:

$$S_n = k[\sin(\varphi + N\alpha) + \sin \varphi \sin N\alpha \sin \tfrac{1}{2}\alpha]$$

$$+ \frac{1}{M}(\gamma_0 \cos N\alpha - \theta_0 \sin N\alpha) + \xi_n - \frac{1}{M} \gamma_N$$

$$C_N = k[\cos(\varphi + N\alpha) - \cos \varphi \sin N\alpha \sin \tfrac{1}{2}\alpha]$$

$$- \frac{1}{M}(\theta_0 \cos N\alpha + \gamma_0 \sin N\alpha) - \eta_N + \frac{1}{M} \theta_N. \tag{57}$$

Comparing these with the ideal outputs:

$$S_N = k \sin\left(\varphi + \frac{N}{M}\right)$$

$$C_N = k \cos\left(\varphi + \frac{N}{M}\right). \tag{58}$$

The errors arising are as follows:

(1) A change of scales of the independent variable input due to taking $\sin \tfrac{1}{2}\alpha = 1/2M$ instead of $\alpha = 1/M$ as in the normal scaling procedure. This error is of order $1/M^3$ and can lead to a drift in phase of about one unit or quantum in M^2 steps.

(2) The truncation terms $k \sin \varphi \sin N\alpha \sin \tfrac{1}{2}\alpha$, $k \cos \varphi \sin N\alpha \sin \tfrac{1}{2}\alpha$ which are due to the finite step size. These errors are sinusoidal and can have amplitudes amounting to one quantum.

(3) The terms involving θ_0 and γ_0 which are effects due to the initial R

numbers. These are also sinusoidal and have amplitudes of one or two quanta.

(4) The cumulative round-off terms ξ_n and η_n which will be discussed shortly.

(5) The ordinary round-off terms $-(1/M)\gamma_N$ and $(1/M)\theta_N$ which are, as in the previous examples, the result of ignoring the least significant halves of double length numbers X_N and Y_N.

To examine the behaviour of the cumulative round-off terms ξ_n and η_n the same assumptions may be made about the sequence of remainders γ and θ as before, i.e. that they may all be replaced by their mean value $M/2$. Making this substitution and summing the resulting trigonometrical series the following expressions result:

$$\xi_N = \tfrac{1}{2}(1 - \cos N\alpha + \sin N\alpha)$$
$$\eta_N = \tfrac{1}{2}(-1 + \cos N\alpha + \sin N\alpha) \tag{59}$$

which are also sinusoidal.

Thus, for a sin/cosine loop operating in the sequential mode with a monotonically increasing angular input, all the errors are either sinusoidal or bounded. Hence for these conditions there will be no tendency for the functions to drift systematically from their correct values. However, at any given instant there is an error which may amount to one or two quanta or units.

Substituting these expressions for the cumulative round-off in equations (57) and rearranging:

$$S_N = \left[k \sin(\varphi + N\alpha) + \sin \varphi \sin N\alpha \sin \tfrac{1}{2}\alpha\right]$$
$$+ \frac{1}{M}\left[\left(\frac{M}{2} - \theta_0\right) \sin N\alpha - \left(\frac{M}{2} - \gamma_0\right) \cos N\alpha\right] + \frac{1}{M}\left(\frac{M}{2} - \gamma_N\right).$$
$$C_N = \left[k \cos(\varphi + N\alpha) - \cos \varphi \sin N\alpha \sin \tfrac{1}{2}\alpha\right]$$
$$+ \frac{1}{M}\left[\left(\frac{M}{2} - \theta_0\right) \cos N\alpha + \left(\frac{M}{2} - \gamma_0\right) \sin N\alpha\right] - \frac{1}{M}\left(\frac{M}{2} - \theta_N\right). \tag{60}$$

In this form it may be seen that a real advantage is obtained by starting with R registers half full. Putting θ_0 and γ_0 equal to $M/2$ causes the error components 3 and 4 above to cancel out and a more accurate result is obtained. The only errors then remaining are the truncation effect (component 2) and the simple round-off effect (component 5).

Drift effects may be investigated as in the previous examples by considering a run of N steps forward followed by N steps backward. This involves algebraic manipulation which it is not proposed to include. The result is as one would expect. Drift effects do occur both in phase and amplitude, the order of magnitude being similar to that for the previous examples considered, viz. one or two quanta for an excursion of N steps.

Returning now to simultaneous operation of the integrators the equations defining the form of the solution are now (46) and (48). The same substitution to variables X and Y may be made to give the equations:

$$X_{n+1} - X_n - \frac{1}{M} Y_n = \frac{1}{M^2} \theta_n$$

$$Y_{n+1} - Y_n + \frac{1}{M} X_n = \frac{1}{M^2} \gamma_n. \tag{61}$$

The solution to the homogeneous equations may readily be shown to be of the form:

$$X_n = k^n \sin n\alpha$$
$$Y_n = k^n \cos n\alpha \tag{62}$$

where $k^2 = 1 + 1/M^2$ and $\tan \alpha = 1/M$. Thus, even for motion in the same direction simultaneous operation of the integrators gives an exponentially increasing factor to the sinusoidal solution. Drifts are therefore obtained for simultaneous operation under circumstances which would be drift-free for sequential operation.

4.7 Binary transfer

Whereas in ternary transfer integrators, increments may take three values, viz.: 1, 0 and -1, for binary transfer increments may only take the two values 1 and -1. A sequence of 1's represents full rate increase and a sequence of -1's full rate decrease. Intermediate rates are obtained by altering the proportion of 1's and -1's and, in particular, zero rate is obtained by alternate 1's and -1's.

The basic integrator consists of two registers as before and using binary notation the role of the sign digit in the Y number is changed in that 1 represents a positive number and 0 represents a negative number. 0's and 1's are used for the transfer code, 0 representing a negative increment and 1 a positive increment. For the independent variable increments the arrival of a 1 causes Y to be added to R and the arrival of a 0 causes the complement of Y to be added to R.

Operation is similar to that of integrators using the ternary system. First an increment is added to the Y number to bring it up-to-data. Then either Y or the complement of Y, i.e. $M-Y$, is added to the R number according the value of the X increment. The output increment δZ is 1 if an overflow occurs and:

$$R_{n+1} = R_n + \tfrac{1}{2}(1+\delta X_n) Y_n + \tfrac{1}{2}(1-\delta X_n)(M-Y_n) - M \qquad (63)$$

and δZ is -1 if an overflow does not occur:

$$R_{n+1} = R_n + \tfrac{1}{2}(1+\delta X_n) Y_n + \tfrac{1}{2}(1-\delta X_n)(M-Y_n) . \qquad (64)$$

These two equations may be combined into a single expression for the output increment:

$$\delta Z = -1 + \frac{2}{M} R_n + \tfrac{1}{2}(1+\delta X) Y_n + \tfrac{1}{2}(1-\delta X_n)(M-Y_n) - R_{n+1} . \qquad (65)$$

Making the substitution:

$$y_n = Y_n - \frac{M}{2} \qquad (66)$$

and simplifying, the following expression is obtained for the output increment:

$$\delta Z = \frac{2}{M} y_n \delta X_n + \frac{2}{M} (R_n - R_{n+1}) \qquad (67)$$

which is the simple integration formula for a single integrator.

The interpretation of the substitution of equation (66) is that zero integrand corresponds to a half-full Y register. A register less than half-full is equivalent to a negative number. Thus the digit of greatest significance is 1 for a positive number and 0 for a negative number as explained previously.

The equations for a sin/cosine schematic may be easily derived and are, in fact:

$$X_{n+1} - X_n - \frac{2}{M} Y_n = \frac{4}{M^2} \theta_n$$

$$Y_{n+1} - Y_n + \frac{2}{M} X_n = \frac{4}{M^2} \gamma_{n+1} . \qquad (68)$$

These equations are of the same form as those for the ternary transfer system and consequently have the same form of solution. There is, however, a difference in the scaling in that the angular increment a is now given by:

$$\sin \frac{\alpha}{2} = \frac{1}{M} \qquad (69)$$

which makes it roughly twice as large as for ternary transfer.

For full rate inputs either positive or negative of the independent variable the solution will be, apart from the change in scaling factor, of exactly the same form as for ternary transfer systems. For intermediate rates and zero rate, drift will tend to occur for the binary transfer system since true zero increments cannot be obtained and input reversals will occur. In ternary transfer systems true zero increments can be obtained, and for intermediate and zero rates these input reversals will not occur. Thus for ternary transfer, drifts will tend to be less even though the defining equations are of the same form as for binary transfer.

4.8 Improvements in incremental processes

It has been shown that the basic cause of truncation error in incremental processes is due to taking a first-order approximation for the increment of the function in terms of the increment of the independent variable. For example, in finding the change in $\cos \theta$ and $\sin \theta$ in terms of the change in θ the following expressions are used:

$$\sin(\theta + \delta\theta) = \sin \theta + \cos \theta \, \delta\theta$$

$$\cos(\theta + \delta\theta) = \cos \theta - \sin \theta \, \delta\theta . \qquad (70)$$

For a finite $\delta\theta$ these expressions are, of course, only approximate and further terms involving $(\delta\theta)^2$, $(\delta\theta)^3$, ... have been neglected. These neglected terms are the basic cause of truncation errors. Drift errors arise mainly because, in the equations (70) the most significant terms to be neglected are those involving $(\delta\theta)^2$.

Accuracy may be improved by the inclusion of a second-order term in the incremental process and, what is more, drift effects will be considerably reduced since the most significant error term now involves $(\delta\theta)^3$ which changes sign with change of the sign of $\delta\theta$. Two courses are now open; one may keep the increment size the same and have increased accuracy, or one may keep the accuracy the same and increase the maximum allowable increment size. The latter alternative gives the advantage of an increased maximum rate of change of the variables for a given speed of operation of the computer in addition to a reduction of the drift effect.

This second possibility of improvement is of great interest to designers of incremental machines and a brief description will now be given of how the process may be applied to the computation of $\sin \theta$ and $\cos \theta$.

In order to see to what extent the size of the increment can be increased by the addition of a second-order term the general expression for the change in $\sin \theta$ may be written:

$$\sin(\theta + \delta\theta) = \sin\theta + \cos\theta\,\delta\theta - \tfrac{1}{2}\sin\theta(\delta\theta)^2 - \tfrac{1}{6}\cos\theta(\delta\theta)^3 + \ldots . \qquad (71)$$

Using the first order term the error made at each step is of the order of $\tfrac{1}{2}(\delta\theta)^2$. If, however, the second order term is included, the error made at each step is of the order of $\tfrac{1}{6}(\delta\theta)^3$. Thus, if the increment used for the first-order formula is $\delta\theta$, the use of the second-order formula would allow the increment to be increased to $n\delta\theta$, while still maintaining the same accuracy, where:

$$\tfrac{1}{6}(n\delta\theta)^3 = \tfrac{1}{2}(\delta\theta)^2 \qquad (72)$$

hence:

$$n = \left(\frac{3}{\delta\theta}\right)^{\frac{1}{3}} . \qquad (73)$$

Equation (73) gives the increase in increment size which can be allowed by the use of the second term while keeping the truncation error constant. The following table gives values of n and increment sizes for various accuracies.

Table 4.2

Accuracy	$\delta\theta$		n	$n\delta\theta$
1 part in	Radians	Minutes of arc		
2^7	2^{-7}	$27'$	7·26	$3° 16$
2^{10}	2^{-10}	$3·3'$	14·53	$50'$
2^{13}	2^{-13}	$0·42'$	29·07	$12'$

This table may be most conveniently explained by a discussion of the first line. For an accuracy of one part in 2^7 or 1 in 256 it is necessary to take an angular increment of 2^{-7} of a radian or 27 minutes of arc using the simple first-order integration formula. The inclusion of the second-order term allows the maximum increment size to be increased by a factor of 7·26 to a value of $3°16'$. It may be noted that, although the multiplying factor increases with increased precision, the maximum allowable increment size decreases. Keeping the integration step rate constant, n is a measure of the allowable increase in the step size which may be obtained by the use of the second-order formula.

An important implication of the use of a second-order term is that now the increment size itself must be capable of variation in magnitude up to its maximum allowable value. It would be no use at all to have an incremental system in which the independent variable increment only took one value, i.e. the maximum allowable. This system would lack the required precision because of the lack of precision in the determination of the independent variable itself rather than because of truncation errors. This situation, of course, does not arise in the case of the first-order formula because the maximum allowable value of the independent variable increment is one unit or quantum and obviously cannot be decreased.

In order to make such an incremental device using a second-order formula one first writes down the formulae:

$$\sin(\theta + \delta\theta) = \sin\theta + \cos\theta\,\delta\theta - \tfrac{1}{2}\sin\theta\,\delta\theta^2$$
$$\cos(\theta + \delta\theta) = \cos\theta - \sin\theta\,\delta\theta - \tfrac{1}{2}\cos\theta\,\delta\theta^2\ . \tag{74}$$

Substituting X_n, Y_n for $\sin\theta$ and $\cos\theta$ respectively, and X_{n+1}, Y_{n+1} for $\sin(\theta + \delta\theta)$ and $\cos(\theta + \delta\theta)$ respectively results in the following difference equations for the incremental process:

$$X_{n+1} = X_n + Y_n\delta\theta - \tfrac{1}{2}X_n\delta\theta^2$$
$$Y_{n+1} = Y_n - X_n\delta\theta - \tfrac{1}{2}Y_n\delta\theta^2 \tag{75}$$

which may be written in the form:

$$X_{n+1} = X_n + (Y_n - \tfrac{1}{2}X_n\delta\theta)\delta\theta$$
$$Y_{n+1} = Y_n - (X_n + \tfrac{1}{2}Y_n\delta\theta)\delta\theta\ . \tag{76}$$

Alternatively, writing the second equation in (74) as:

$$\cos(\theta + \delta\theta) = \cos\theta - \sin(\theta + \delta\theta)\theta + \tfrac{1}{2}\cos\theta\,\delta\theta^2 \tag{77}$$

the difference equations may be written:

$$X_{n+1} = X_n + (Y_n - \tfrac{1}{2}X_n\delta\theta)\delta\theta$$
$$Y_{n+1} = Y_n - (X_{n+1} - \tfrac{1}{2}Y_n\delta\theta)\delta\theta\ . \tag{78}$$

From these equations it may be seen that the incorporation of a second-order term can be implemented by performing two incremental operations at each stage of integration instead of one. For instance, to carry out the steps of the first equation of (78), one would first calculate $Y_n - \frac{1}{2}X_n \delta\theta$ and then calculate $X_n + (Y_n - \frac{1}{2}X_n \delta\theta)\delta\theta$. This indicates that some process rather like the first-order integration process could be used.

Since, however, $\delta\theta$ may now be more than one unit, it follows that in general a multiplication is required for the calculation of $X_n \delta\theta$ etc. This may be avoided if it is always arranged so that the number of units in $\delta\theta$ is always a power of 2. In this case, the calculation of expressions of the form $X_n + K\delta\theta$ may be performed by adding in the quantity K at some suitable level of significance to the quantity X_n. Even further simplification is achieved to limit $\delta\theta$ to have only two values, one some power of two times the other. This would result in a coarse-fine system and would be little less effective and if completely general values of $\delta\theta$ were permitted.

4.9 The second-order incremental process

A briefly description of a sin/cosine computer using second-order incremental processes is now given. The general functional diagram is shown in Figure 4.9.

The angular or independent variable input is taken to be in whole number form from a shaft digitizer which is sampled once per computing cycle. In the particular realization of the device described here the basic computing cycle or step is divided into four equal timing periods, A_1, A_2, A_3, A_4, controlling waveforms generating these periods being produced by a timing pulse generator.

The first operation to be performed is to decide what sort of increment has occurred since the last computing cycle, and this is done by comparing the present value of the digitizer output with the previous value. At some point in the cycle period A_3 would be suitable, the digitizer is read into the shift register SR1. During A_4 the contents of SR1 and SR2 are passed via the gates 1 and 3 through an adder/subtractor which puts out the difference. This difference goes via the gate 6 to a discriminator which decides whether a coarse or fine increment is required and also the sign of the increment. This information then passes to the increment store which holds it for a computing cycle which starts at A_1.

During period A_1 the increment is also transmitted to one of the inputs of the adder/subtractor and added to the contents of SR2, the sum being

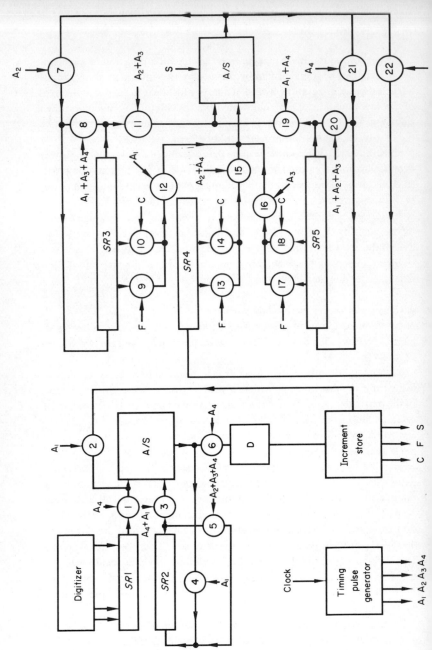

Figure 4.9. *Second-order incremental computer.*

circulated back into SR2 via gate 4. During periods A_2, A_3, A_4, the contents of SR2 are circulated unchanged via the gate 5. The behaviour of the SR2 number is thus to follow the output of the digitizer and for a constant output it will catch up by a series of coarse increments followed by fine increments until the two numbers are equal. The SR2 number will always synchronize itself ultimately with the digitizer output, but whereas during a single cycle the digitizer output may change by an arbitrary amount, the SR2 number only changes by a coarse or a fine increment.

Thus the increment has been determined for the next computing cycle which begins at A_1. This increment is held in a store and applied to the arithmetic side of the computer. Shift registers SR3 and SR4 are double length and hold the current values of X and Y respectively and during A_1 the computation of $Y_n - 1/2X_n\delta\theta$ takes place. This is achieved by taking an output from SR3 via gate 9 or 10 according to whether a fine or coarse increment respectively is required to one input of the adder/subtractor, the other input being taken from the least significant end of SR5. The positions of gates 9 and 10 are chosen so that the SR3 and the SR4 numbers are combined at the correct relative significance in the adder/subtractor to give $Y_n - 1/2X_n\delta\theta$. This is possible since $\delta\theta$ is some negative power of 2 whether the increment is coarse or fine.

The function of the adder/subtractor is determined by the sign output S of the increment store and its output is transmitted to SR4 via gate 22. Meanwhile the contents of SR3 and SR4 are recirculated back via gates 8 and 20. Thus, at the end of period A_1 the contents of SR3, SR4 and SR5 are X_n, $Y_n - 1/2X_n\delta\theta$ and Y_n respectively.

During periods A_2 the SR3 number X_n and the SR4 number $Y_n - 1/2X_n\delta\theta$ are combined in the adder/subtractor via gates 11 and 15 respectively to give $X_n + (Y_n - 1/2X_n\delta\theta)\delta\theta$ which is equal to X_{n+1} and which is circulated into SR3 via gate 7. Thus, at the end of A_2 the contents of SR3 and SR4 are X_{n+1} and 0 respectively. The contents of SR5 are recirculated via gate 20 during this period.

During periods A_3 and A_4 similar operations occur with SR3 and SR5 interchanged leaving X_{n+1} in SR3 and Y_{n+1} in SR5, and this completes the incremental step.

The device may be made to be self-synchronizing by the introduction of gating which simultaneously sets up SR2 and SR3 equal to 0 and SR5 equal to 1. This corresponds to setting in the conditions $\theta = \sin\theta = 0$ and $\cos\theta = 1$. The automatic follow-up action of the SR2 number will then cycle the contents of the registers to correspond to the output of the digitizer. Thus this device, in addition to having the improvements to be obtained by the use of a second-order incremental formula, also has a self-setting up feature. This self-setting up facility is made practical by the increased speed performance which may be obtained by the use of the second-order formula. Typically, for an accuracy of about 0·1 per cent one can achieve synchronization in about a $\frac{1}{12}$ of a second, whereas for a first-order formula synchronization would take about a second.

4.10 Conclusion

In this chapter a general method has been described for the error analysis of d.d.a. schematics using the basic mathematical tool of the calculus of finite differences. While the method is of perfectly general application it has been found more enlightening to apply it to specific schematics, namely simple integration, multiplication by a constant, squaring, the exponential function, sine and cosine.

The basic causes of d.d.a. errors have been found to be due to truncation and round-off. Truncation arises because of the finite step size of the integration process and round-off is caused by the finite step size in the digital representation of the variables. For the simple integrator the main component in the truncation error is due to the second-order term in the expansion of the increment of the function in terms of the independent variable and this gives rise to the well known integrator drift phenomenon.

Round-off effects are more difficult to analyse and it has been necessary to take a statistical approach which has given very good results for the types of inputs which are likely to be met with in practice. The assumption made in this chapter that the series of remainder terms can be replaced by their mean values may be shown to be valid provided that the amplitudes of the input oscillations are a reasonable number of quanta. This however, is not the complete answer as it is possible to get complex correlation effects for small oscillations of the order of one or two quanta in amplitude. Nevertheless for practical applications it is a reasonable working rule.

Most of the analysis has been carried out in terms of the ternary transfer system of increments, but one schematic has also been formulated in binary transfer. It is found that, apart from a change in scale factor the basic difference equations are identical in form for both cases. In spite of this, however, the binary transfer operation is more prone to drift because of spurious oscillations produced by the nature of the binary transfer process.

The sin/cosine schematic has been formulated in terms of both sequential and simultaneous operation of integrators, and changes in the drift characteristics are noted. The most significant effect occurs for monotonic inputs. Whereas for sequential operation it is shown that all the errors are sinusoidal in form, for simultaneous operation systematic drift occurs. For inputs with reversals, systematic drift occurs for both types of operation. Thus in error analysis the type of operation whether it be sequential or simultaneous can be significant.

Integrator operation may be improved by the introduction of a second-order term into the process. The obvious effect of this is either to increase accuracy or to increase speed by increasing the maximum allowable size of the input increment. A slightly less obvious effect, but nevertheless highly significant one, is the reduction of drift. Having introduced the second-order term, the most significant truncation contribution is now of the third order in the independent variable increment. This term changes sign with input reversal and consequently does not build up with input oscillations.

Introduction of the second-order term leads to integrator operation similar to d.d.a. operation and an incremental device for computing sine and cosine is described. Because of the increase of speed obtainable it is possible to think in terms of whole number input followed by a differencing process and also to have a self-synchronizing facility. In order to preserve the essential simplicity of the d.d.a. approach a coarse/fine treatment of the incremental input is used which enables the second-order processes to be carried by the use of addition only.

5: Sampled Data Theory Applied to the D.D.A.

5.1 Introduction
In Chapter 4 a method of analysing the behaviour of some d.d.a. schematics based on the manipulation of finite difference equations is given. The method is analogous to the conventional solution of linear differential equations in terms of a 'complementary function' and a 'particular integral'.

An alternative method in the theory of linear differential equations is obtained from the use of the Laplace transform [1]. The Laplace transform has the property that the differential operator transforms into the Laplace operator. As a result the transformed equation can be rearranged to express the transformed output as a function of the Laplace operator. The solution is thus reduced to four simple operations:

(i)   performing the Laplace transform, using tables;
(ii) rearranging to obtain the transform of the result;
(iii) manipulating this transform into partial fractions and
(iv) performing the inverse transform using the tables.

This method may also be applied to the solution of linear difference equations. In this case the integral transform reduces to a summation and in this form is referred to as the Z transform.

The Z transform is, in some respects, easier to understand than the Laplace transform and so we begin by introducing the Z transform in its own right. Some of the properties of the transform are developed and applied to the solution of simple d.d.a. schematics.

In the second half of the chapter the relationship between the Z transform and the Laplace transform is deduced and the behaviour of the d.d.a. in the time domain is considered. The idea of the transfer function (familiar in the theory of linear servo systems) is used to develop the concept of frequency response and stability. As might be expected digital systems are subject to more severe stability limitations. This point is illustrated by an example of the use of a d.d.a. integrator as part of a servo control system.

The following symbols and notation are used throughout this chapter:

a	Constant (undefined)
c	Integrator constant (paragraph 5.2.3.)
E	Advance operator $(E[f_n] = f_{n+1})$
f_n	Function of n (paragraph 5.2.1)
$G(s)$	The transfer function of a system
$G*(s) = G(z)$	The starred (or Z) transfer function of a system
$h(t)$	The hold function (paragraph 5.4.2.)
i_n	Dependent variable input to an integrator or system
$j = \sqrt{(-1)}$	Imaginary operator
k	Variable integer
$\mathcal{L}$	Laplace transform operator
n	Iteration suffix (integer)
o_n	Output of an integrator or system
r_n	Round-off of an integrator
s	Laplace operator
t_n	Independent variable input to an integrator
u_n	Unit step function (paragraph 5.2.1)
$V(E^{-1})$	Operator (equation 13)
w	Frequency of input function
$z = e^{-s}$	The z operator
Z	The Z transform operator
$\delta(t-n)$	The sampling function (equation 25)
$\nabla = 1 - E^{-1}$	Backward difference operator $(\nabla[f_n] = f_n - f_{n-1})$
*	A star superfix indicates a sampled function

Throughout capital letters are used to denote transforms thus:

$$H(s) \equiv \mathcal{L}[h(t)]$$
$$F*(s) \equiv \mathcal{L}[f*(t)]: \quad F(z) \equiv Z[f_n]$$
$$I*(s) \equiv \mathcal{L}[i*(t)]: \quad I(z) \equiv Z[i_n]$$
$$O*(s) \equiv \mathcal{L}[o*(t)]: \quad O(z) \equiv Z[o_n]$$
$$R(z) \equiv Z[r_n]$$

5.2 The d.d.a. as an algebraic operator

In this section we shall define the Z transform, derive some of its properties and apply it to the d.d.a. to obtain similar results to those in Chapter 4. In common with most transform techniques the method has the merit of reducing the calculations to simple algebraic manipulations but suffers from the disadvantage that it obscures the essential nature of the system to some extent. The method is introduced here partly to provide an alternative approach to the problems and therefore (it is hoped) greater insight into them. Chiefly, however, the method is described as an introduction to the more generalized transient response analysis.

In the literature [1] it is conventional to introduce the Z transform as a special case of the Laplace transform arising from the use of sampled functions. The present author has deliberately refrained from this practice for two reasons. Firstly the Z transform should be recognized as having a value independent of its relationship with the Laplace transform. Secondly the introduction of the Laplace transform is an unnecessary complication to those who are interested in algebraic relationships only. Those who still prefer the alternative approach should read the later sections of the chapter first.

5.2.1 *Definitions*

In the first part of this chapter we are concerned with functions f_n of the integral (iteration) suffix n. The functions are arbitrarily defined as zero for all negative n, thus:

$$f_n = 0: \quad n < 0 .$$

It should be noted that, at this stage, we are not concerned with the time dependence of n or with the behaviour of f_n between iterations.

It is convenient to define the term unit 'step' function by:

$$u_n = \begin{cases} 1: & n \geqslant 0 \\ 0: & n < 0 . \end{cases}$$

5.2.2 *The Z transform*

Given a function of the type defined above we shall define the Z transform of the function by:

$$F(z) \equiv Z[f_n] \equiv \sum_{n=0}^{\infty} f_n . z^n . \tag{1}$$

This definition is in conformity with that used by Salzer [2, 3]. Other authors [1] use a definition based on z^{-1} instead of z. The inverse transform may be defined by the implicit relation:

$$f_n \equiv Z^{-1}[F(z)] . \tag{2}$$

We shall not concern ourselves here with the conditions under which the Z transform and its inverse exist.

To maintain the continuity of the argument and to assist the reader unfamiliar with Z transform theory, a number of properties of the Z transform will now be deduced for use in the later parts of the chapter.

From the definition of the Z transform (equation (1)) it is seen that:

$$Z[a^n] = \sum_{n=0}^{\infty} a^n z^n = \frac{1}{1-az} \tag{3}$$

whence the transform of the unit step function is (putting $a=1$):

$$Z[u_n] = \frac{1}{1-z}. \tag{4}$$

Now:

$$Z[nf_n] = \sum_{n=0}^{\infty} nf_n z^n = z \sum_{n=0}^{\infty} f_n nz^{(n-1)}$$

$$= z \sum_{n=0}^{\infty} f_n \frac{d}{dz}(z^n)$$

$$= z\left[\frac{d}{dz} \sum_{n=0}^{\infty} f_n z^n\right]$$

$$Z[nf_n] = z\left[\frac{d}{dz} F(z)\right]. \tag{5}$$

Applying equation (5) to equation (3) we have:

$$Z[na^n] = z\left[\frac{d}{dz}\left(\frac{1}{1-az}\right)\right] = \frac{az}{(1-az)^2} \tag{6}$$

and applying it again to (6) we have:

$$Z[n^2 a^n] = z\left[\frac{d}{dz}\left(\frac{az}{(1-az)^2}\right)\right] = \frac{az(1+az)}{(1-az)^3}. \tag{7}$$

Defining the advance operator E by: $E(f_n) \equiv f_{n+1}$ we have

$$Z[E(f_n)] = \sum_{n=0}^{\infty} f_{n+1} z^n.$$

Putting $k=n+1$. we have:

$$Z[E(f_n)] = z^{-1}\left[\sum_{k=0}^{\infty} f_k z^k - f_0\right]$$

$$= z^{-1}[F(z) - f_0]. \tag{8}$$

Also:

$$Z[E^{-1}(f_n)] = \sum_{n=0}^{\infty} f_{n-1} z^n = z \sum_{n=0}^{\infty} f_{n-1} z^{n-1}.$$

Since by definition f_n is zero for negative n we have, (putting $k=n-1$):

$$Z[E^{-1}(f_n)] = z \sum_{k=0}^{\infty} f_k z^k = z F(z).$$

From this we can write down the following result:

$$Z[V(E^{-1})f_n] = V(z)F(z) \tag{9}$$

and defining the backward difference operator by:

$$\nabla = 1 - E^{-1}$$

we have from equation (9)

$$Z[\nabla f_n] = (1-z)F(z). \tag{10}$$

Finally:

$$Z[a^n f_n] = \sum_{n=0}^{\infty} f_n (az)^n = F(az). \tag{11}$$

These are all the results we shall require for this chapter and they are given in Table 5.1.

5.2.3 *The d.d.a. integrator*

Assuming a sequential d.d.a. and defining all functions in relation to a discrete iteration cycle commencing at the first integrator, we may write down an expression for the output of the integrator at the nth iteration using backward difference operators:

$$\nabla(o_n + r_n) = t_n V(E^{-1}) i_n \tag{12}$$

where $V(E^{-1})$ is the operator:

$$V(E^{-1}) = \begin{cases} 1 & : \text{ rectangular} \\ \frac{1}{2}(1 + E^{-1}) & : \text{ trapezoidal} \end{cases} \tag{13}$$

and the variables are:

output: o_n
input (dependent variable): i_n
round-off: r_n
independent variable (increments): t_n (14)

Table 5.1 *Z-Transforms*

Equation number	f_n	$Z(f_n)$
(1)	f_n	$\sum_{n=0}^{\infty} f_n z^n$
(2)	$Z^{-1}[F(z)]$	$F(z)$
(3)	a^n	$\dfrac{1}{(1-az)}$
(4)	u_n	$\dfrac{1}{(1-z)}$
(5)	nf_n	$z\left[\dfrac{d}{dz}F(z)\right]$
(6)	na^n	$\dfrac{az}{(1-az)^2}$
(7)	$n^2 a^n$	$\dfrac{az(1+az)}{(1-az)^3}$
(8)	$E[f_n]=f_{n+1}$	$z^{-1}[F(z)-f_0]$
(9)	$V(E^{-1})f_n$	$V(z)F(z)$
(10)	∇f_n	$(1-z)F(z)$
(11)	$a^n f_n$	$F(az)$

The right-hand side of equation (12) represents the 'integration' function carried out by the integrator and this is equated to the change in the output and round-off terms. Scale factors are implicit in the variables r_n and t_n.

Taking the Z transform of equation (12) using Table 5.1 (equation 10) we have:

$$(1-z)[O(z)+R(z)] = Z[t_n V(E^{-1})i_n]$$

where capital letters signify Z transforms (e.g. $O(z)=Z(o_n)$), whence:

$$O(z)+R(z) = \frac{1}{1-z}\{Z[t_n V(E^{-1})i_n]\} \tag{15}$$

and the inverse transform is:

$$o_n+r_n = Z^{-1}\left(\frac{1}{1-z}\{Z[t_n V(E^{-1})i_n]\}\right). \tag{16}$$

The round-off term is exhibited as a step function output. If the behaviour of r_n is predictable analytically or statistically, its effect on the next integrator can be calculated. We shall neglect the effect of round-off in the remainder of this chapter. Two important cases will be analysed further:

Case 1: $t_n = c$.
This is the case of the ordinary integrator and from equations (16) and (9) (Table 5.1) neglecting r_n:

$$o_n = cZ^{-1}\left[\frac{V(z)\,I(z)}{1-z}\right]. \tag{17}$$

If the transfer function $G(z)$ of the integrator is defined as the ratio of the Z transform of the output to the Z transform of the input (or alternatively as the Z transform of the response of the system to a unit impulse at the first iteration):

$$o_n = Z^{-1}[G(z)\,I(z)] \tag{18}$$

where
$$G(z) = \begin{cases} \dfrac{c}{1-z} & : \text{rectangular} \\[2ex] \dfrac{c\frac{1}{2}(1+z)}{(1-z)} & : \text{trapezoidal} \end{cases} \tag{19}$$

Example 1. If the input is a ramp function:

$$i_n = n$$

then from Table 5.1 equation (6):

$$I(z) = \frac{z}{(1-z)^2}$$

so that for the rectangular integrator:

$$G(z) = c/(1-z)$$

$$O(z) = G(z)I(z) = \frac{cz}{(1-z)^3}.$$

Taking partial fractions [1]:

$$O(z) = \tfrac{1}{2}c\left[\frac{z(z+1)}{(1-z)^3} + \frac{z}{(1-z)^2}\right]$$

and performing the inverse transform:

$$o_n = \tfrac{1}{2}c[n^2+n].$$

In the case of a trapezoidal integrator:

$$O(z) = G(z)\,I(z) = \tfrac{1}{2}c\,\frac{z(z+1)}{(1-z)^3}$$

$$o_n = \tfrac{1}{2}cn^2.$$

This simple problem is the solution for the conventional use of an integrator as a squarer. Used in this way the rectangular integrator can be regarded as giving rise to a truncation or 'drift' error of amount $\tfrac{1}{2}cn$ whereas the trapezoidal process is exact in this case (the constant $\tfrac{1}{2}c$ can be taken care of in the scaling).

Case 2: $t_n = (-1)^n c.$

This is the case of the integrator with a binary zero independent variable. Using equation (11) Table 5.1 and neglecting r_n, equation (16) becomes:

$$o_n = cZ^{-1}\left[\frac{V(-z)\,I(-z)}{(1-z)}\right] \tag{20}$$

where

$$\frac{cV(-z)}{(1-z)} = \begin{cases} \dfrac{c}{(1-z)} & : \text{rectangular} \\[2mm] \tfrac{1}{2}c & : \text{trapezoidal}. \end{cases} \tag{21}$$

It should be noted that these functions are not transfer functions in the sense defined above (i.e. they are not the ratio of the Z transform of the output to the Z transform of the input).

Example 2. Suppose that we have a binary zero input variable:

$$i_n = \tfrac{1}{2}[1+(-1)^n].$$

From Table 5.1 equation (3):

$$I(z) = \tfrac{1}{2}\left[\frac{1}{1-z} + \frac{1}{1+z}\right]$$

$$= \frac{1}{1-z^2}$$

$$= I(-z).$$

For a rectangular integrator with a binary zero independent variable:

$$Z^{-1}\left[\frac{V(-z)I(-z)}{1-z}\right] = Z^{-1}\left[\frac{1}{(1-z)^2(1+z)}\right]$$

$$= Z^{-1}\left\{\left(\frac{\frac{1}{2}z}{(1-z)^2}+\frac{\frac{1}{2}}{1-z}\right)+\left[\frac{\frac{1}{4}}{1-z}+\frac{\frac{1}{4}}{1+z}\right]\right\}$$

$$= \tfrac{1}{2}(n+1)+\tfrac{1}{4}[1+(-1)^n].$$

This is the case of the binary integrator with zero variable inputs. The term in square brackets is the characteristic oscillation of the binary integrator. The other term is the phenomenon referred to as drift.

In the case of the trapezoidal integrator:

$$Z^{-1}\left[\frac{V(-z)I(-z)}{1-z}\right] = Z^{-1}[\tfrac{1}{2}I(-z)]$$

$$= \tfrac{1}{2}i_n$$

and the integrator is seen to be drift free although still retaining the characteristic binary oscillation.

5.2.4 *Series and closed loop configurations*

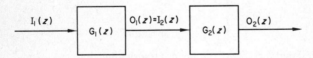

Figure 5.1. *Transfer functions in series.*

Consider two blocks in series with transfer functions $G_1(z)$ and $G_2(z)$ as in Figure 5.1. The output transform of the first block is by definition:

$$O_1(z) = G_1(z)I_1(z)$$

and the output transform of the second block is:

$$O_2(z) = G_2(z)I_2(z) = G_2(z)G_1(z)I_1(z)$$

so that the transfer function of the two blocks in series is by definition:

$$G(z) = \frac{O_2(z)}{I_1(z)} = G_1(z)G_2(z). \qquad (22)$$

Example 3. Suppose that we have two rectangular integrators in series, then from (22) the transfer function is:

$$G(z) = \frac{c^2}{(1-z)^2}.$$

Suppose that the input is: $i_n = e^n$.

From Table 5.1:
$$I(z) = \frac{1}{1-ez}.$$

So that:
$$O(z) = G(z)I(z) = \frac{c^2}{(1-z)^2} \cdot \frac{1}{1-ez}.$$

Now by partial fractions:

$$O(z) = \frac{c^2}{(1-e)^2}\left[\frac{(1-e)z}{(1-z)^2} + \frac{1-2e}{1-z} + \frac{e^2}{1-ez}\right]$$

whence finding the inverse transforms using Table 5.1 we have:

$$o_n = \frac{c^2}{(1-e)^2}\left[(1-e)n + (1-2e) + e^{n+2}\right].$$

Note that this solution also exhibits a drift term $(1-e)n$.

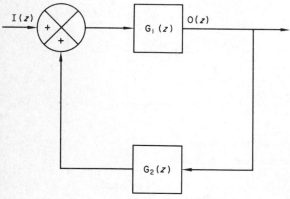

Figure 5.2. Feedback configuration of transfer functions.

With the simple feedback system in Figure 5.2, from equation (22) it can be seen that:

$$O(z) = G_1(z)[I(z) + G_2(z)O(z)]$$

so that the transfer function of the complete loop is:

$$G(z) = \frac{O(z)}{I(z)} = \frac{G_1(z)}{1 - G_1(z)G_2(z)}. \qquad (23)$$

This result and equation (22) are identical in form to those that occur in the theory of linear servomechanisms.

Example 4. Consider the rectangular integrator with feedback (Figure 5.3). The feedback path offers a single iteration interval delay to the output

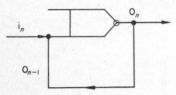

(a) *Schematic diagram.*

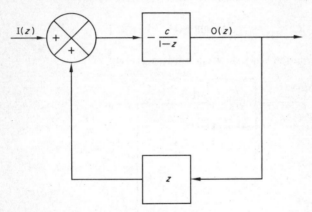

(b) *Equivalent transfer function diagram.*

Figure 5.3. *The single integrator with feedback.*

before feeding it back to the input. Thus from equation (9) the transfer function of the feedback path can be written as z.

From equation (23) the transfer function of the rectangular integrator with feedback is:

$$G(z) = \frac{-c}{1 - z(1 - c)}.$$

Putting:
$$1-c=e^{-a}$$

we have:
$$G(z) = -\frac{1-e^{-a}}{1-ze^{-a}}.$$

The response of the system to a unit step function at iteration 1 is therefore:

$$o_n = Z^{-1}\left[\frac{e^{-a}-1}{(1-ze^{-a})}\cdot\frac{1}{(1-z)}\right]$$

$$= Z^{-1}\left[\frac{e^{-a}}{(1-ze^{-a})} - \frac{1}{(1-z)}\right]$$

$$= e^{-(n+1)a}-1.$$

Note that if c is small $a \simeq c$ and:

$$o_n \simeq e^{-(n+1)c}-1.$$

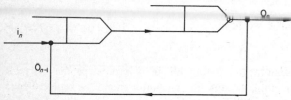

(a) Schematic diagram.

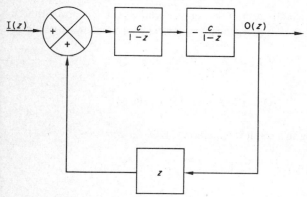

(b) Equivalent transfer function diagram.

Figure 5.4. The sin/cosine loop.

Example 5. The conventional sin/cosine loop (Figure 5.4) may be analysed in a similar way. The transfer function of the loop is given by:

$$G(z) = \frac{-c^2}{(1-z)^2 + c^2 z}.$$

If we put:
$$\cos a = \tfrac{1}{2}(e^{ja} + e^{-ja}) = \tfrac{1}{2}(2 - c^2)$$

we can write:
$$G(z) = -\frac{2(1-\cos a)}{(1 - z e^{-ja})(1 - z e^{ja})}$$

$$= -\frac{2(1-\cos a)}{(e^{ja} - e^{-ja})}\left[\frac{e^{ja}}{(1 - z e^{ja})} - \frac{e^{-ja}}{(1 - z e^{-ja})}\right]$$

and the inverse transform (impulse response) is:

$$-\frac{2 \sin^2 \tfrac{1}{2}a}{j \sin a}\left(e^{(n+1)ja} - e^{-(n+1)ja}\right) = -2 \tan \tfrac{1}{2}a \sin(n+1)a.$$

Note that for small c we have $c \simeq a$ and the response is approximately $-c \sin(n+1)c$.

Example 6. The case of the integrator with binary zero independent variable is rather more intractable because the integrator cannot be replaced by a transfer function. However each case can be examined by applying equation (20).

Suppose we take the case of the simple rectangular integrator with feedback and a binary zero independent variable. Using equation (20) we have:

$$O(z) = -\frac{c}{1-z}[I(-z) - z O(-z)]. \tag{24}$$

Hence:
$$O(-z) = -\frac{c}{1+z}[I(z) + z O(z)]$$

and substituting this result in equation (24) we have:

$$O(z) = -\frac{c}{1-z}\left[I(-z) + \frac{cz}{1+z}\{I(z) + z O(z)\}\right].$$

Collecting terms and rearranging we have:

$$O(z) = -\frac{c[(1+z)I(-z) + cz\,I(z)]}{1 - z^2(1 - c^2)}.$$

If we let the input be the unit impulse function at iteration 1 then $I(z) = I(-z)$ $= 1$ and:

$$O(z) = -\frac{c[1 + z(1 + c)]}{1 - z^2(1 - c^2)} .$$

Putting $a = (1 - c^2)^{\frac{1}{2}}$

$$O(z) = -\frac{c}{2a}\left[\frac{a + (1 + c)}{1 - za} + \frac{a - (1 + c)}{1 + za}\right].$$

From Table 5.1 performing the inverse transform we have:

$$o_n = -ca^{n-1}\tfrac{1}{2}\{[a + (1 + c) + (-1)^n[a - (1 + c)]\}$$

$$= \begin{cases} -ca^n & : n \text{ even} \\ -ca^{n-1}(1 + c): & n \text{ odd}. \end{cases}$$

The previous examples are all concerned with sequential machines. The same techniques may be used for simultaneous integrators but, in general, the results will be different. This is because in a simultaneous machine the output of any integrator suffers a unit iteration delay before it is used by any other integrator. A good example of this is the sin/cosine loop of Figure 5.4(a) using simultaneous integrators. In this case the characteristic equation has complex roots and the solution is exponentially unstable.

5.3 The transient response of the d.d.a. integrator

So far we have concerned ourselves only with the concept of the d.d.a. as an algebraic operator using the method of Z transforms to obtain solutions similar to those obtained by difference equation techniques in Chapter 4. The solutions have been obtained in terms of the iteration suffix n and no assumptions have been made about the time dependence of n. If the time dependence of n is defined then it is a simple matter to insert this in the appropriate solutions. However, if the d.d.a. is used as part of an overall control system it may be necessary to understand its relationship to continuous external elements. The theory of sampled data systems extends the use of Laplace transforms in linear system theory to that of sampled systems.

5.3.1 *Sampled data system theory*

We shall now assume that, as is the case with the conventional, sequential d.d.a.,:

(i) The operations are carried out in real time at a constant sampling rate. In terms of our earlier notation:

$$t_n = 1$$

where the constant iteration period is defined as the unit of time.

(ii) The time delay due to computation is negligible.

Let us now consider the computer as acting on continuous functions $f(t)$ with the unit sampling function $\delta(t-n)$ defined by:

$$\int_0^\infty f(t)\,\delta(t-n)\mathrm{d}t = \sum_{n=0}^\infty f(n). \tag{25}$$

We shall now define the starred function $f^*(t)$ as the sampled function:

$$f^*(t) = f(t)\,\delta(t-n) \tag{26}$$

and consider the Laplace transform defined by:

$$F^*(s) = \mathscr{L}f^*(t) = \int_0^\infty f^*(t)\,\mathrm{e}^{-st}\mathrm{d}t. \tag{27}$$

From this and equation (26) we have:

$$F^*(s) = \int_0^\infty f(t)\,\delta(t-n)\,\mathrm{e}^{-st}\mathrm{d}t$$

which in view of (25) becomes:

$$F^*(s) = \sum_{n=0}^\infty f(n)\,\mathrm{e}^{-ns}. \tag{28}$$

It will be observed that equation (28) is identical to equation (1) if we put:

$$z = \mathrm{e}^{-s}. \tag{29}$$

Thus with this definition of z:

$$F^*(s) \equiv F(z). \tag{30}$$

An alternative definition to equation (28) which gives further insight into the meaning of the Z transform is obtained by considering the Fourier series representation of the unit sampling function $\delta(t-n)$. Thus let:

$$\delta(t-n) = \sum_{k=-\infty}^\infty a_k\,\mathrm{e}^{jk2\pi t}.$$

The Fourier coefficients a_k are given by:

$$a_k = \int_{-\frac{1}{2}}^{\frac{1}{2}} \delta(t-n)\,e^{-jn2\pi t}\,dt = 1\;.$$

Thus:

$$\delta(t-n) = \sum_{k=-\infty}^{\infty} e^{jk2\pi t}\;. \tag{31}$$

Hence from equation (26):

$$f^*(t) = f(t) \sum_{k=-\infty}^{\infty} e^{jk2\pi t}$$

and from (27)

$$F^*(s) \equiv \mathscr{L}f^*(t) = \int_0^{\infty} \left[f(t) \sum_{k=-\infty}^{\infty} e^{jk2\pi t} \right] e^{-st}\,dt$$

$$= \sum_{k=-\infty}^{\infty} \int_0^{\infty} f(t)\,e^{-(s-jk2\pi)t}\,dt$$

and so from (27):

$$F^*(s) = \sum_{k=-\infty}^{\infty} F(s-jk2\pi)\;. \tag{32}$$

Thus from equations (30) and (32) we have the identity:

$$F^*(s) \equiv F(z) \equiv \sum_{n=0}^{\infty} f(n)z^n$$

$$\equiv \sum_{k=-\infty}^{\infty} F(s-jk2\pi)\;. \tag{33}$$

We now deduce two important properties of the functions defined by equation (33).

(i) *Periodicity*

It is clear from equation (33) that for any integer k:

$$F^*(s+jk2\pi) = F^*(s)\;. \tag{34}$$

That is to say that the starred function is periodic in the frequency domain and is defined by the strip of the complex s-plane between the lines $\pm j\pi$.

(ii) *Conjugate symmetry*

Since:

$$e^{-ks} = e^{-k(\sigma \pm jw)} = e^{-k\sigma}(\cos kw \pm j \sin kw)$$

if e^{-ks} is defined for positive real frequencies it is also defined for negative real frequencies. It follows that $F^*(s)$ also has conjugate symmetry. Hence it suffices to define $F^*(s)$ between the lines 0 and $j\pi$.

Since the function $F^*(s)$ is completely defined if it is defined in the region bounded by the lines 0 to $j\pi$, it follows that frequencies in excess of π in the original function will not be recoverable. This is the same limitation on bandwidth as that established by the sampling theorem [5, 6] which states that: 'If a function f(t) contains no frequencies higher than w c/s, it is completely determined by giving its ordinates at a series of points spaced $1/2w$ seconds apart.'

5.3.2 *Frequency response*

Consider a transfer function $G(z)$, the Z transform of the output response to a sinusoidal input is given from equation (18) and Table 5.1 by:

$$O(z) = G(z)\frac{1}{1-z\,e^{jw}}.$$

This may be split up into partial fractions of the form:

$$O(z) = \frac{A}{1-z\,e^{jw}} + B(z)$$

where $B(z)$ has the same numerator as $G(z)$. Now if we multiply by $1-z\,e^{jw}$ and put $z = e^{-jw}$ (i.e. $s = jw$) we have:

$$A = G(e^{-jw}).$$

Thus: $$O(z) = \frac{G(e^{-jw})}{1-z\,e^{jw}} + B(z).$$

In the steady state, provided the impulse response of the system is a decaying function of time, the term due to $B(z)$ will vanish as t tends to infinity. The steady-state frequency response of $G(z)$ is therefore given by:

$$o(w) = G(e^{-jw})e^{njw}. \qquad (35)$$

Thus the amplitude of the output is $G(e^{-jw})$ times that of the input and is phase shifted by an amount $\underline{/G(e^{-jw})}$. Hence from equation (19), putting $z = e^{-jw}$ the response of the rectangular integrator to a sinusoidal input is given by:

$$G(e^{-jw}) = \frac{1}{1-e^{-jw}}$$

$$= \tfrac{1}{2} \operatorname{cosec} \tfrac{1}{2}w \, e^{j\frac{1}{2}(w-\pi)}$$

$$= \tfrac{1}{2}[1 - j \cot \tfrac{1}{2}w].$$

Thus the amplitude term is $\tfrac{1}{2} \operatorname{cosec} \tfrac{1}{2}w$ and the phase of the output is $\tfrac{1}{2}(w-\pi)$.

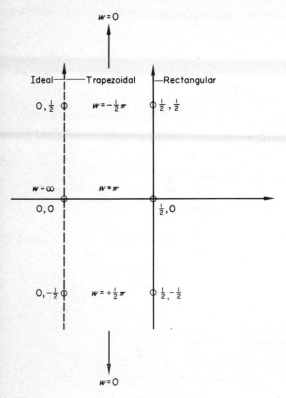

Figure 5.5. Comparison of integrator loci.

The function $1/(1-z)$ is plotted in the complex s-plane in Figure 5.5 and the amplitude and phase are plotted in Figures 5.6 and 5.7. In the case of the trapezoidal integrator from equation (19), putting $z = e^{-jw}$, the response of the integrator to a sinusoidal input is given by:

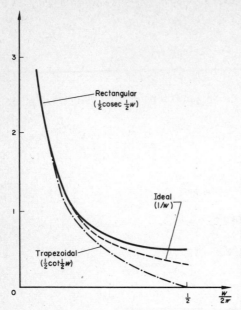

Figure 5.6. Amplitude characteristics of integration rules.

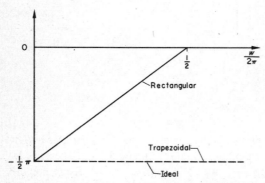

Figure 5.7. Phase characteristics of integration rules.

$$G(e^{-jw}) = \tfrac{1}{2} \frac{(1+e^{-jw})}{(1-e^{-jw})}$$

$$= \tfrac{1}{2} \cot \tfrac{1}{2}w \, e^{-j\frac{1}{2}\pi}.$$

This function is also shown in Figure 5.5 and the amplitude and phase are shown in Figures 5.6 and 5.7.

The ideal integrator has a Laplace transform $1/s$ and the frequency response is $1/jw$. The ratios of the frequency response amplitudes for the rectangular and trapezoidal integrators to that of the ideal integrator are:

rectangular: $\tfrac{1}{2}w \operatorname{cosec} \tfrac{1}{2}w$

trapezoidal: $\tfrac{1}{2}w \cot \tfrac{1}{2}w$.

Two points should be observed in relation to the rectangular and trapezoidal integrator frequency responses:

(i) The ratio of the amplitude characteristic to that of the ideal integrator is greater than one for the rectangular integrator and less than one for the trapezoidal integrator. This is clear from Figure 5.6.

(ii) There is a phase error $\tfrac{1}{2}w$ in the rectangular integrator whereas the trapezoidal integrator has ideal phase (Figure 5.7).

Thus the trapezoidal integrator, in addition to having ideal phase tends to attenuate the high frequencies and may therefore be more desirable than the rectangular integrator in the presence of noise.

5.4 The d.d.a. in control

In the previous section we considered some of the properties of the integrator in the time domain. These properties are only of academic interest unless the computer has a relationship with some external time-dependent system. In this section we shall describe the properties of typical interface units between the computer and its inputs and outputs and then derive some of the relations applicable to mixed analogue and digital systems showing the effect of sampling on the stability of a simple, mixed system.

5.4.1 *Inputs*

Conventional computers for control have various forms of input media. In each case the d.d.a. is essentially acting as a sampling device and the computer looks at the sampled function $i^*(t)$, so that we may make use of the starred or Z transform to express the operation of the computer on the input

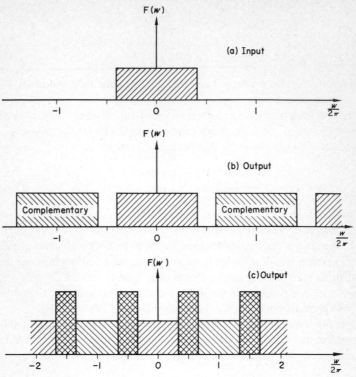

Figure 5.8. *Effect of sampling on the input frequency spectrum.*

function. From equation (33) the action of sampling is characterized in the
s-domain by:

$$F^*(s) = \sum_{k=-\infty}^{\infty} F(s-jk2\pi).$$

Thus the application of a signal of complex frequencies results in an output
component which is the exact input, and additional output components of
frequencies differing from it by integral multiples of the sampling frequency
(2π). This is illustrated in the idealized diagrams of Figures 5.8(a) and (b).

As pointed out by Salzer [2] a digital computer program cannot have low-
pass characteristics. If it has a pass band in the range 0 to π it will also have a
pass band in the region of frequencies $2k\pi$ where k is any integer. The presence

of these so-called complementary signals may be undesirable in a control system. It will be shown below that one of the functions of the output converter is to filter out the complementary signals.

It is apparent from the above (and intuitively obvious) that the iteration rate sets a limit on the effective bandwidth of the digital filter. A faster iteration rate can be said to give a greater bandwidth.

A further effect which deserves careful attention is the possible presence of signal frequencies in the range π to 3π. In this case equation (33) shows that it is possible to mix in spurious complementary terms in the range 0 to π. If the amplitude of these complementary terms is significant they will have a profound effect on the output signal. Figure 5.8(c) shows how reducing the iteration frequency in Figure 5.8(b) (or increasing the input frequency band in Figure 5.8(a)) induces complementary signals which destroy the characteristic of the output function. In general it will be necessary to use either a higher iteration rate or (if this is not available) a filter to remove the higher input frequencies before they enter the digital computer.

5.4.2 *Outputs*
After each iteration the d.d.a., like any other digital computer, holds or remembers the last results. Thus the output of any given integrator can be described by:

$$o(t) = o(n): \qquad n \leqslant t < n+1.$$

The unit impulse response of this function is shown in Figure 5.9. It follows

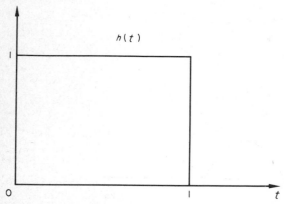

Figure 5.9. *Response of the hold function to a unit impulse.*

that the Laplace transform of this function is given by:

$$H(s) = \int_0^1 e^{-st}\,dt$$

$$= \frac{1}{s}(1-e^{-s})$$

$$= \frac{1}{s}(1-z). \tag{36}$$

Substituting $s = jw$ we obtain from equation (36):

$$H(jw) = \frac{1}{jw}(1-e^{jw})$$

$$= -\frac{1}{2j}(e^{\frac{1}{2}jw} - e^{-\frac{1}{2}jw})\frac{e^{\frac{1}{2}jw}}{\frac{1}{2}w}$$

$$= -\frac{\sin\frac{1}{2}w}{\frac{1}{2}w}e^{\frac{1}{2}jw}. \tag{37}$$

Thus this filter introduces a linear phase error of $\frac{1}{2}w$ and the amplitude response $\sin\frac{1}{2}w/\frac{1}{2}w$ is shown in Figure 5.10. It is seen that the hold function

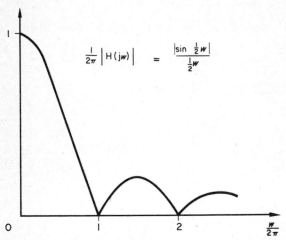

Figure 5.10. *Frequency response of the hold function.*

is essentially a low-pass filter which passes the low frequency spectrum of the impulse train and helps to attenuate the complementary high frequencies resulting from the sampling process.

5.4.3 *The transfer function of a sampled data system*

Suppose now that we have a system consisting of a linear filter followed by a sampler (Figure 5.11). The transfer function of the filter, $G(s)$, is defined by:

$$O(s) = G(s) I(s) \tag{38}$$

and the starred transform of the output is given from equation (33) by:

$$O^*(s) = \sum_{k=-\infty}^{\infty} G(s+jk2\pi) I(s+jk2\pi). \tag{39}$$

It should be noted that in this case:

$$O^*(s) \neq G^*(s) I^*(s). \tag{40}$$

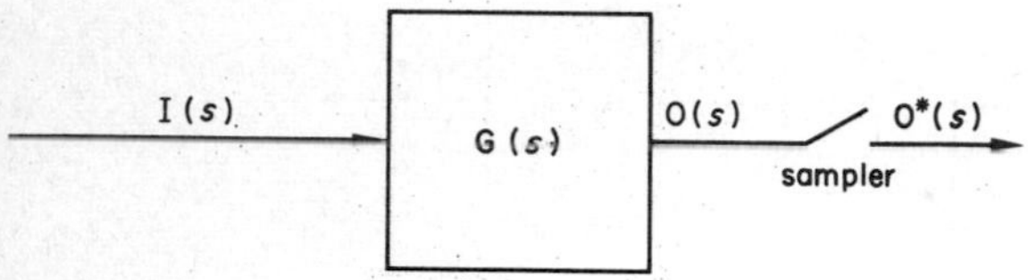

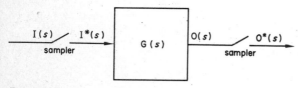

Figure 5.11.

Figure 5.12.

However if we now put a sampler in front of the linear filter as in Figure 5.12 equation (38) becomes:

$$O(s) = G(s) I^*(s) \tag{41}$$

whence equation (39) becomes:

$$O^*(s) = \sum_{k=-\infty}^{\infty} G(s+jk2\pi) I^*(s+jk2\pi) \tag{42}$$

and using (34):

$$O^*(s) = I^*(s) \sum_{k=-\infty}^{\infty} G(s+jk2\pi) \tag{43}$$

which from (33) gives:

$$O^*(s) = G^*(s)I^*(s). \tag{44}$$

It follows from equation (44) that the starred transfer functions for series and feedback arrangements of linear digital filter functions (or more generally functions separated by a sampler) are identical in algebraic form to those for linear continuous filters. In view of equation (30) this is a result which could have been anticipated from equation (22). This relation and equation (23) can be used to find the transfer function of any combination of d.d.a. integrators.

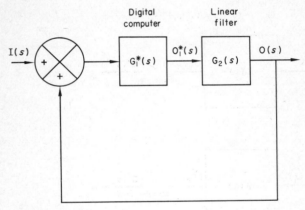

Figure 5.13. A sampled data system.

In systems where the digital computer forms a part of an overall control system including linear filters we have to use relations derived from equation (39). Ragazzini and Zadeh [3] give a table of Laplace and starred (or Z) transforms for linear systems including one or more samplers. We shall content ourselves here with deriving a relation for the system defined by Figure 5.13. From equation (23):

$$\frac{O_1^*(s)}{I^*(s)} = \frac{G_1^*(s)}{1 - G_1^*(s)G_2^*(s)}.$$

So that:

$$O(s) = G_2(s)O_1^*(s)$$

$$= \frac{G_2(s)G_1^*(s)I^*(s)}{1 - G_1^*(s)G_2^*(s)} \tag{45}$$

and from equation (44) the starred transfer function is:

$$\frac{O^*(s)}{I^*(s)} = \frac{G_1^*(s)G_2^*(s)}{1 - G_1^*(s)G_2^*(s)}. \tag{46}$$

5.4.4 *Comparison of a linear and a sampled data system*

To illustrate the way in which a digital filter can be expected to behave we shall compare a simple analogue system consisting of an integrator and a simple filter in the feedback path (Figure 5.14a) with the same system using a d.d.a. to perform the integration (Figure 5.14b). As we have already seen, we should expect a difference in behaviour due to the effects of sampling. Indeed it will be shown that whereas the simple analogue system is always stable provided the feedback is negative, the equivalent digital system is unstable if the loop gain is increased beyond a certain finite value.

Considering the simple analogue system first of all (Figure 5.14a), it can be shown that the transfer function is [1]:

$$\frac{G_1(s)}{1 + G_1(s)G_2(s)}$$

where:

$$G_1(s)G_2(s) = \frac{a}{s(s+1)} = a\left[\frac{1}{s} - \frac{1}{s+1}\right].$$

Using the method of partial fractions the transfer function may be split into terms of the form:

$$\frac{A}{s+\alpha} + \frac{B}{s+\beta}$$

and the inverse transform or impulse response is then:

$$A e^{\alpha t} + B e^{\beta t}$$

where α and β are the roots of the characteristic equation:

$$1 + G_1(s)G_2(s) = 0.$$

That is:

$$s(s+1) + a = 0.$$

Clearly, the system will be stable if neither of the roots has a positive real part. The roots of the equation are:

$$[-1\pm(1-4a)^{\frac{1}{2}}]/2$$

and a positive root will exist if, and only if, a is negative. Thus the system is non-divergent provided that the feedback is negative. This may also be demonstrated by the Nyquist plot of $G_1(jw)G_2(jw)$ where stability is deter-

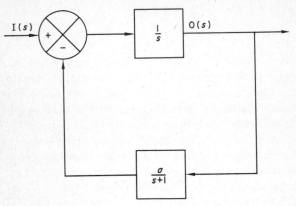

(a) Analogue system.

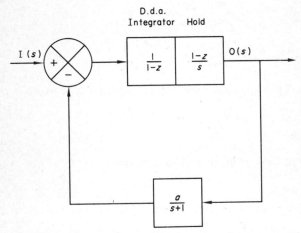

(b) System using a d.d.a. integrator.

Figure 5.14. Comparison of an analogue and a sampled data system.

mined by whether the Nyquist plot encloses the point $(-1, 0)$. Figure 5.15 shows the plot of $a^{-1}G_1(jw)G_2(jw)$. It will be seen that since the plot passes through the origin for $w = \infty$ the system will not enclose the point $(-1, 0)$ for any value of a, so that the system is again seen to be stable for negative feedback.

Now consider the system shown in Figure 5.14(b). From equation (46) the starred transfer function is:

$$\frac{O^*(s)}{I^*(s)} = \frac{G_1^*(s)}{1 + G_1^*(s)G_2^*(s)}$$

where
$$G_1^*(s)G_2(s) = \frac{a}{s(s+1)} = a\left[\frac{1}{s} - \frac{1}{s+1}\right].$$

So that
$$\mathscr{L}^{-1}[G_1^*(s)G_2(s)] = a[1 - e^{-t}]$$

and from Table 5.1:

$$G_1^*(s)G_2^*(s) = a\left[\frac{1}{1-z} - \frac{1}{1-e^{-1}z}\right]$$

$$-\frac{a(1-e^{-1})z}{(1-z)(1-e^{-1}z)}. \tag{47}$$

The transfer function may be split into partial fractions of the form:

$$\frac{O^*(s)}{I^*(s)} = \frac{A}{1-e^{-\alpha}z} + \frac{B}{1-e^{-\beta}z}$$

and the inverse transform or impulse response is then $Ae^{-n\alpha} + Be^{-n\beta}$ where e^α, e^β are the roots of the characteristic equation:

$$1 + G_1^*(s)G_2^*(s) = 0.$$

From (47) this gives:

$$z^2 - z[e+1-a(e-1)] + e = 0.$$

Clearly, the impulse response will be divergent if either of the roots has a modulus less than one. The roots of the characteristic equation are:

$$z = \tfrac{1}{2}\{[e+1-a(e-1)] \pm \sqrt{[e+1-a(e-1)]^2 - 4e}\}.$$

Inspection of these roots shows that the solution is divergent ($|z| < 1$) for values of a defined by:

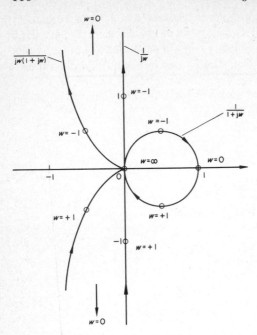

Figure 5.15. Nyquist diagram for the analogue system.

$$0 > a > \frac{2(e+1)}{e-1}.$$

This may also be demonstrated by the Nyquist plot of $G_1^*(e^{-jw})G_2^*(e^{-jw})$ where stability is determined by whether the Nyquist plot encloses the point $(-1, 0)$. Figure 5.16 shows that since the plot with $a=1$ passes through the abscissae at $\frac{1}{2}(e-1)/(e+1)$ the system will be divergent for $a > 2(e+1)/(e-1)$.

The above criterion is concerned solely with absolute stability. Thus for $a=2(e+1)/(e-1)$ one of the terms in the impulse response of the system is $(-1)^n$. Even for smaller values of a the system behaviour would be unsatisfactory for practical purposes. Secondly it must be remembered that the results are concerned with the behaviour of the system at the sampling instants only. In some systems it is possible for oscillations to occur at multiples of the iteration frequency. Such behaviour would not be revealed by the above analysis. The treatment of such cases is described in the literature [7, 8].

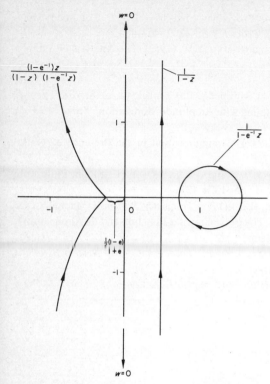

Figure 5.16. *Nyquist diagram for system using a d.d.a. integrator.*

5.5 Conclusion

This chapter is not an exhaustive treatment of the application of sampled data theory to d.d.a.'s. The author's purpose will have been served if the chapter acts as an introduction to the theory of sampled data systems to those familiar with the d.d.a. or vice versa. Those interested in more complex problems such as the synthesis of stable systems should refer to the literature [9].

References

[1] ASELTINE, J. A. (1958) *Transform Method in Linear System Analysis*, McGraw-Hill.

[2] SALZER, J. M. (1954) 'Frequency Analysis of Digital Computers Operating in Real Time', *Proc. I.R.E.*, **42**, 2, 457–466.

[3] RAGAZZINI, J. R. and ZADEH, L. A. (1952) 'The Analysis of Sampled Data Systems', *Trans. A.I.E.E.*, **71**, II, 225–232, See also discussion on pp. 232–234.

[4] LINVILL, W. K. (1951) 'Sampled-Data Control Systems Studied Through Comparison of Sampling with Amplitude Modulation', *Trans. A.I.E.E.*, **70**, II, 1779–1788.

[5] SHANNON, C. E. (1949) 'Communication in the Presence of Noise', *Proc. I.R.E.* **37**, 10–21.

[6] OLIVER, B. M., PIERCE, J. R. and SHANNON, C. E. (1948) 'The Philosophy of PCM', *Proc. I.R.E.*, **36**, 1324–1331.

[7] OLDENBURGER, R., (Ed.) (1956) *Frequency Response*, Macmillan Co. N.Y., pp. 325–341. 'The Pulse Transfer Function and its Application to Sampling Servosystems'.

[8] TRUXAL, J. G. (1955) *Automatic Feedback Control System Synthesis*, McGraw-Hill, Chapter 9.

[9] TOU, J. T. (1959) *Digital and Sampled Data Control Systems*, McGraw-Hill.

6: The Problems of Aircraft Stability and Control

6.1 Introduction

One important aspect of aeronautical research and development which requires extensive use of computing aids is the investigation of aircraft stability and control problems. It is natural therefore to determine what contribution the d.d.a. can make in this field. The basic computing exercise in the study of stability and control is the solution of six non-linear differential equations; three force equations which relate the motion of the aircraft centre of gravity to the external force components resolved relative to a Cartesian axis system, and three moment equations relating the rotations about the centre of gravity to the external moment components. The solutions of these equations should ideally be presented in the form of a continuous record of the acceleration and velocity components enabling the periods, amplitudes and dampings of the resultant motion to be analysed. This suggests an analogue type of computing system and therefore the d.d.a. with its analogue type of solution and digital repeatability and accuracy should be ideally suited to this task.

Many extensions of the basic exercise are of interest. Equations representing autopilot systems may be added enabling autopilot characteristics to be studied. The motion of an aircraft relative to earth or another aircraft may be required to enable estimates of miss distances in missile studies to be made. This chapter demonstrates how these and the six basic equations can be set up and solved on the d.d.a.

The programs described are suitable for solution on any d.d.a., sequential or simultaneous, binary or ternary, and the programming techniques employ the notation and sub-programs developed in Chapter 3.

6.2 The equations of motion

The motion of the aircraft can be conveniently described relative to the principal body axes of the aircraft. This axis system has its origin at the centre of gravity of the aircraft and moves with the aircraft. The directions of the axes are shown in Figure 6.1. The x–z plane is the plane of symmetry. The

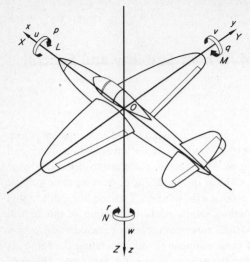

Figure 6.1. Principal body axes and notation.

notation adopted conforms with current aeronautical practice and is set out below:

u v w components of velocity along *Ox Oy Oz*

V resultant velocity

p q r components of angular velocity about *Ox Oy Oz*

X axial force

Y side force

Z normal force

L rolling moment

M pitching moment

N yawing moment

m aircraft mass

A B C moments of inertia about *Ox Oy Oz*

ξ aileron angle

η elevator angle

ζ rudder angle

g acceleration due to gravity

Moments, angular velocities and rotations are taken to be positive when clockwise as viewed in the positive direction of the axis.

The force equations are:

$$X + n_1 mg = m(\dot{u} + qw - rv)$$
$$Y + n_2 mg = m(\dot{v} + ru - pw) \qquad (1)$$
$$Z + n_3 mg = m(\dot{w} + pv - qu)$$

The moment equations are:

$$L - A\dot{p} + (C - B)\, qr$$
$$M = B\dot{q} + (A - C)\, rp \qquad (2)$$
$$N = C\dot{r} + (B - A)\, pq$$

$n_1 n_2 n_3$ are the direction cosines defining the position of the gravity vector relative to Ox, Oy, Oz. They are found by solving the equations:

$$\dot{n}_1 = rn_2 - qn_3$$
$$\dot{n}_2 = pn_3 - rn_1 \qquad (3)$$
$$\dot{n}_3 = qn_1 - pn_2$$

6.3 Representation of the aerodynamics

In order to solve the equations of motion, the aerodynamic contributions to the external forces and moments must be simulated. The aerodynamics may be represented by assuming the aerodynamic forces and moments to be functions of the instantaneous values of the linear and angular velocities, control angles and their derivatives. Thus if A is a typical aerodynamic force moment, the change, A', brought about by a small change in flight conditions is:

$$A' = u' A_u + \dot{u}' A_{\dot{u}} + v A'_v + \dots + \zeta' A_\zeta + \dot{\zeta}' A_{\dot{\zeta}} \qquad (4)$$

where

$$A_u = \left(\frac{\partial A}{\partial u} \right)_o \quad \text{etc.}$$

The subscript o denotes that the derivative is evaluated at the reference, i.e. steady-state flight condition: $u', \dot{u}', v', \zeta', \dot{\zeta}'$ etc. are the changes in $u, \dot{u}, v, \zeta, \dot{\zeta}$, etc. from the initial flight condition. The terms such as A_u are termed the stability derivatives.

Many of the possible derivatives are either zero or negligibly small. For a typical aircraft, the aerodynamics can be generated in terms of the derivatives with significant contributions as follows [1]:

$$\left.\begin{aligned}
X' &= u'X_u + w'X_w \\
Y' &= v'Y_v + p'Y_p + r'Y_r + \zeta'Y_\zeta \\
Z' &= u'Z_u + w'Z_w + \dot{w}'Z_{\dot{w}} + q'Z_q + \eta'Z_\eta
\end{aligned}\right\} \tag{5}$$

$$\left.\begin{aligned}
L' &= v'L_v + p'L_p + r'L_r + \xi'L_\xi + \dot{\xi}'L_{\dot{\xi}} + \zeta'L_\zeta \\
M' &= u'M_u + w'M_w + \dot{w}'M_{\dot{w}} + q'M_q + \eta'M_\eta + \dot{\eta}'M_{\dot{\eta}} \\
N' &= v'N_v + \dot{v}'N_{\dot{v}} + p'N_p + r'N_r + \xi'N_\xi + \zeta'N_\zeta + \dot{\xi}'N_{\dot{\xi}}
\end{aligned}\right\} \tag{6}$$

In many cases further simplification may be possible, depending on the required accuracy of simulation.

The derivatives are estimated mathematically or found from wind tunnel tests [2]. They may be assumed constant for small perturbations about the reference flight condition. For large amplitude motions, the derivatives cannot in general be assumed constant and this method of representation becomes unsound. Nevertheless it is often used for those conditions and can provide valuable results.

6.4 Simulation of the aircraft

The simulation of the aircraft is achieved by solving equations (1), (2) and (3). In general the linear and angular velocities and accelerations will be required. As shown in Chapter 3, the equations have to be expressed in a form suitable for representation on a d.d.a. and become:

$$\left.\begin{aligned}
d\dot{u} &= d\left(\frac{X}{m}\right) + g\,dn_1 - q\,dw - w\,dq + r\,dv + v\,dr \\[2mm]
d\dot{v} &= d\left(\frac{Y}{m}\right) + g\,dn_2 - r\,du - u\,dr + p\,dw + w\,dp \\[2mm]
d\dot{w} &= d\left(\frac{Z}{m}\right) + g\,dn_3 - p\,dv - v\,dp + q\,du + u\,dq
\end{aligned}\right\} \tag{7}$$

$$\left.\begin{aligned}
d\dot{p} &= d\left(\frac{L}{A}\right) - \left(\frac{C-B}{A}\right)q\,dr - \left(\frac{C-B}{A}\right)r\,dq \\[2mm]
d\dot{q} &= d\left(\frac{M}{B}\right) - \left(\frac{A-C}{B}\right)r\,dp - \left(\frac{A-C}{B}\right)p\,dr \\[2mm]
d\dot{r} &= d\left(\frac{N}{C}\right) - \left(\frac{B-A}{C}\right)p\,dq - \left(\frac{B-A}{A}\right)q\,dp
\end{aligned}\right\} \tag{8}$$

$$dn_1 = n_2 r \, dt - n_3 q \, dt$$
$$dn_2 = n_3 p \, dt - n_1 r \, dt \qquad (9)$$
$$dn_3 = n_1 q \, dt - n_2 p \, dt$$

The forces and moments comprise contributions from the aerodynamics, and the engine thrust and torque. Assume the engine contribution to be thrust components T_x T_y T_z relative to Ox Oy Oz and a moment R_y about Oy.

Since $d(X'/m) = d(X/m)$ and $du' = du$, the forces and moments can be computed in the d.d.a. as:

$$d\left(\frac{X}{m}\right) = \frac{X_u}{m} \, du + \frac{X_w}{m} \, dw + d\left(\frac{T_x}{m}\right)$$

$$d\left(\frac{Y}{m}\right) = \frac{Y_v}{m} \, dv + \frac{Y_p}{m} \, dp + \frac{Y_r}{m} \, dr + \frac{Y_\zeta}{m} \, d\zeta + d\left(\frac{T_y}{m}\right) \qquad (10)$$

$$d\left(\frac{Z}{m}\right) = \frac{Z_u}{m} \, du + \frac{Z_w}{m} \, dw + \frac{Z_{\dot{w}}}{m} \, d\dot{w} + \frac{Z_q}{m} \, dq + \frac{Z_\eta}{m} \, d\eta + d\left(\frac{T_z}{m}\right)$$

$$d\left(\frac{L}{A}\right) = \frac{L_v}{A} \, dv + \frac{L_p}{A} \, dp + \frac{L_r}{A} \, dr + \frac{L_\xi}{A} \, d\xi + \frac{L_{\dot{\xi}}}{A} \, d\dot{\xi} + \frac{L_\zeta}{A} \, d\zeta$$

$$d\left(\frac{M}{B}\right) = \frac{M_u}{B} \, du + \frac{M_w}{B} \, dw + \frac{M_{\dot{w}}}{B} \, d\dot{w} + \frac{M_q}{B} \, dq + \frac{M_\eta}{B} \, d\eta + \frac{M_{\dot{\eta}}}{B} \, d\dot{\eta} + d\left(\frac{R_y}{B}\right)$$

$$d\left(\frac{N}{C}\right) = \frac{N_v}{C} \, dv + \frac{N_{\dot{v}}}{C} \, d\dot{v} + \frac{N_p}{C} \, dp + \frac{N_r}{C} \, dr + \frac{N_\xi}{C} \, d\xi + \frac{N_\zeta}{C} \, d\zeta + \frac{N_{\dot{\xi}}}{C} \, d\dot{\xi}$$

$$(11)$$

The flow diagrams for the solution of the pitching moment equation and the direction cosine equations, including generation of the aerodynamics, are given in Figures 6.2 and 6.3. The incremental inputs representing change of thrust, change of control angle and rate of change of control angle can, if required, be produced by additional computations. For example, the control inputs may be provided by a program simulating an autopilot. As dn_1, dn_2, dn_3, etc. are required as integrator ΔX inputs, hard adders are included in Figure 6.3 to provide these increments on single lines. The adders produce a change of sign of the increments.

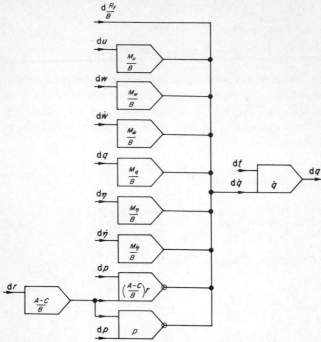

Figure 6.2. Solution of pitching moment equation to give acceleration.

The complete program for solution of equations (7), (8), (9), (10) and (11) requires 74 integrators. More integrators, programmed as hard adders, may be necessary if the design of the computers is such that the integrators do not have sufficient ΔY inputs or ΔZ outputs.

If the acceleration terms are not required as whole numbers the program can be simplified. The d.d.a. force and moment equations can be written as:

$$\left.\begin{aligned}
\mathrm{d}u &= \left(\frac{X}{m}\right)\mathrm{d}t + n_1 g\,\mathrm{d}t - wq\,\mathrm{d}t + vr\,\mathrm{d}t \\[2mm]
\mathrm{d}v &= \left(\frac{Y}{m}\right)\mathrm{d}t + n_2 g\,\mathrm{d}t - ur\,\mathrm{d}t + wp\,\mathrm{d}t \\[2mm]
\mathrm{d}w &= \left(\frac{Z}{m}\right)\mathrm{d}t + n_3 g\,\mathrm{d}t - vp\,\mathrm{d}t + uq\,\mathrm{d}t
\end{aligned}\right\} \qquad (12)$$

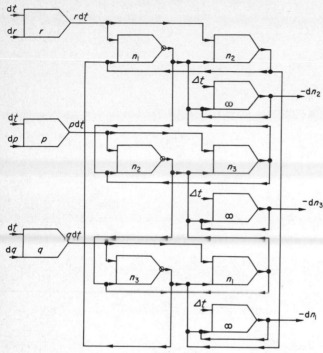

Figure 6.3. Direction cosine equations.

$$dp = \left(\frac{L}{A}\right) dt - \left(\frac{C-B}{A}\right) qr\, dt$$

$$dq = \left(\frac{M}{B}\right) dt - \left(\frac{A-C}{B}\right) rp\, dt \qquad (13)$$

$$dr = \left(\frac{N}{C}\right) dt - \left(\frac{B-A}{C}\right) pq\, dt$$

For most economical use of integrators the aerodynamic terms are treated as follows. Consider for example $(X/m)dt$. Since $u' = u - u_0$, etc. then:

$$\frac{X}{m} dt = \frac{X_0}{m} dt + \frac{X_u}{m}(u-u_0)dt + \frac{X_w}{m}(w-w_0)dt + \frac{T_x}{m} dt \qquad (14)$$

thus:

$$\frac{X}{m}\,dt = \frac{X^*}{m}\,dt + \frac{X_u}{m}\,u\,dt + \frac{X_w}{m}\,w\,dt + \frac{T_x}{m}\,dt \tag{15}$$

where:

$$X^* = X_0 - X_u u_0 - X_w w_0 \tag{16}$$

i.e. X^* is constant.

Treating the remaining aerodynamic terms similarly:

$$\frac{X}{m}\,dt = \frac{X^*}{m}\,dt + \frac{X_u}{m}\,u\,dt + \frac{X_w}{m}\,w\,dt + \frac{T_x}{m}\,dt$$

$$\frac{Y}{m}\,dt = \frac{Y^*}{m}\,dt + \frac{Y_v}{m}\,v\,dt + \frac{Y_p}{m}\,p\,dt + \frac{Y_r}{m}\,r\,dt + \frac{Y_\zeta}{m}\,\zeta\,dt + \frac{T_y}{m}\,dt \tag{17}$$

$$\frac{Z}{m}\,dt = \frac{Z^*}{m}\,dt + \frac{Z_u}{m}\,u\,dt + \frac{Z_w}{m}\,w\,dt + \frac{Z_{\dot{w}}}{m}\,dw + \frac{Z_q}{m}\,q\,dt + \frac{Z_\eta}{m}\,\eta\,dt + \frac{T_z}{m}\,dt$$

$$\frac{L}{A}\,dt = \frac{L^*}{A}\,dt + \frac{L_v}{A}\,v\,dt + \frac{L_p}{A}\,p\,dt + \frac{L_r}{A}\,r\,dt + \frac{L_\xi}{A}\,\xi\,dt + \frac{L_{\dot{\xi}}}{A}\,d\xi + \frac{L_\zeta}{A}\,\zeta\,dt$$

$$\frac{M}{B}\,dt = \frac{M^*}{B}\,dt + \frac{M_u}{B}\,u\,dt + \frac{M_w}{B}\,w\,dt + \frac{M_{\dot{w}}}{B}\,dw + \frac{M_q}{B}\,q\,dt + \frac{M_\eta}{B}\,\eta\,dt$$

$$\qquad\qquad + \frac{M_{\dot{\eta}}}{B}\,d\eta + \frac{R_y}{B}\,dt \tag{18}$$

$$\frac{N}{C}\,dt = \frac{N^*}{C}\,dt + \frac{N_v}{C}\,v\,dt + \frac{N_{\dot{v}}}{C}\,dv + \frac{N_p}{C}\,p\,dt + \frac{N_r}{C}\,r\,dt + \frac{N_\xi}{C}\,\xi\,dt$$

$$\qquad\qquad + \frac{N_\zeta}{C}\,\zeta\,dt + \frac{N_{\dot{\xi}}}{C}\,d\zeta .$$

The direction cosine equations remain unchanged. The complete program for the solution of equations (9), (12), (13), (17) and (18) requires 66 integrators.

The aircraft velocity V is generally required.

$$V = (u^2 + v^2 + w^2)^{\frac{1}{2}} . \tag{19}$$

This equation is solved using the normal square and square root schematic. In d.d.a. equation form:

$$(V-1)\,dV - u\,du - v\,dv - w\,dw = -dV. \tag{20}$$

6.5 Scaling

The principles of elementary scaling are described in Chapter 3. Here the application of those principles to more complex equations is demonstrated. To avoid the use of detailed, numbered flow diagrams for all the equations, the scale constants etc. of all the variables will be defined by taking the symbols for the variables as subscripts. For example, the scale constant for u will be k_u.

The first requirement is to list the maximum values of all the terms appearing in integrator Y registers. For a low-speed aeroplane the dominant term in the equations will probably be uZ_u/m, for a high-speed vehicle where high angular velocities can occur, the major aerodynamic term affecting the scaling is likely to be vL_v/A, while the dominant term in the equations will probably be qu.

A typical problem is the scaling of the flow diagram giving accelerations when uZ_u/m is the major term. The direction cosine schematic must be considered first:

$$K_c = N_c K_c K_q \mathrm{d}t \tag{21}$$

where subscript c refers to the direction cosines.

Thus:
$$K_{q\mathrm{d}t} = \frac{1}{N_c}. \tag{22}$$

In general $p\,\mathrm{d}t$, $q\,\mathrm{d}t$ and $r\,\mathrm{d}t$ can have the same scale constant, which, from equation (22) must be a power of two.

Since the maximum value of a direction cosine is 1

$$K_c > 1/N_c \tag{23}$$

The scaling of the direction cosine flow diagram is similar to that of a sine/cosine loop.

As uZ_u/m is the major term in the equations, the normal force equation is next considered.

$$K_{\dot{w}} = M_{z_u} K_u \tag{24}$$

The second most important term in the normal force equation is qu. As, in general N_u will be larger than N_q:

$$K_{\dot{w}} = N_u K_u K_q. \tag{25}$$

Now
$$K_q = M_{\dot{q}} K_t. \tag{26}$$

If the simulation is required in real time K_t will be defined as $1/I$ where I is the iteration rate in iterations per second. Then eliminating all the scale constants except K_t from equations (24), (25), (26):

$$\frac{M_{z_u}}{N_u M_{\dot{q}} K_t} = 1. \tag{27}$$

This condition must be satisfied.

However, the accuracy of the computation is generally more important than the time scale:

$$K_{q\text{d}t} = M_q K_t. \tag{28}$$

Eliminating all scale constants from equations (22), (24), (25), (26), (28) gives:

$$\frac{M_{z_u} M_q N_c}{M_{\dot{q}} N_u} = 1. \tag{29}$$

This condition replaces equation (27) and will in general give better scaling. A further condition must be satisfied.

$$K_u = M_{\dot{u}} K_t \tag{30}$$

$$K_u = \frac{M_u}{N_u}. \tag{31}$$

Eliminating all the scale constants from equations (22), (28), (30), (31):

$$\frac{M_u M_q N_c}{M_{\dot{u}} N_u} = 1. \tag{32}$$

As the problem maxima of all the variables are known, values can be assigned which satisfy the conditions. If high computational accuracy is desired the values of N will be chosen as large as possible. For optimum scaling $M_{z_u} M_q M_{\dot{q}} M_u M_{\dot{u}}$ should correspond closely to the problem maxima. Values of M assigned during the rest of the scaling may be larger than the problem maxima. When the conditions are satisfied numbers can be calculated for all the terms in equations (21) to (32). The time scale extension the ratio of real time to problem time is $1/IK_t$.

To complete the exercise the normal and axial force equations, and finally the moment equations, are scaled. The scaling follows a similar procedure.

6.6 Autopilots

In many missile simulations an autopilot will form an essential part of the program. Such an autopilot channel is shown diagrammatically in Figure 6.4 where a demanded rate of turn r_d is compared with the body rate of turn

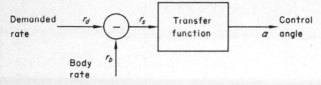

Figure 6.4. Autopilot channel.

r_b. The difference $(r_d - r_b)$ is related to the control angle a by a transfer function. A typical transfer function is of the form:

$$\frac{a}{r_d - r_b} = \frac{A + BP}{P^3 + CP^2 + DP + E} \tag{33}$$

where $P - \partial/\partial t$, and A, B, C, D and E are constants.

The d.d.a. equation corresponding to equation (33) is

$$d(\ddot{a}) = A r_d dt - A r_b dt + B dr_d - B dr_b - C d\dot{a} - D da - E a dt \tag{34}$$

r_b and $r_b dt$ are available from the solutions of the equations of motion. r_d and $r_d dt$ the demand inputs, will be generated by an additional computation. $d\dot{a}$ and da, or da, and $a dt$ will be passed to the integrators generating the control angle contributions to the aerodynamics.

Typically there will be three autopilot channels controlling motion in roll, when r_b is p and a is ξ in pitch when r_b is q and a is η in yaw where r_b is r and a is ζ. The transfer functions for each channel may differ.

As the autopilot can be represented by differential equations its simulation by the d.d.a. presents no fundamental difficulties. As its frequencies are much higher than those of the aircraft the accuracy of representation is correspondingly less.

6.7 Axis transformations

Thus far the solutions of the equations of motion have been presented relative to the aircraft body axes. Motion relative to other axes, for example an earth fixed axis system, is often of interest.

The conventional earth fixed axes are an orthogonal right-handed system $Ox_E\,y_E\,z_E$ with the positive Oz_E axis vertically upwards.

The aircraft's components of acceleration due to the external forces are in body axes:

$$\left.\begin{aligned}
\dot{u}_o &= \frac{X}{m} - n_1\,g \\[2mm]
\dot{v}_o &= \frac{Y}{m} - n_2\,g \\[2mm]
\dot{w}_o &= \frac{Z}{m} - n_3\,g
\end{aligned}\right\} \tag{35}$$

where $n_1\,n_2\,n_3$ are the direction cosines of Oz_E with respect to $O\,x\,y\,z$, and $X\,Y\,Z$ include aerodynamic and engine contributions.

The transformation equations are conveniently presented in matrix form. If $\dot{v}_B^{BE}$ is the matrix of the acceleration of the aircraft relative to earth in body axes:

$$\dot{v}_B^{BE} = \begin{bmatrix} \dot{u}_o \\ \dot{v}_o \\ \dot{w}_o \end{bmatrix} \tag{36}$$

then the acceleration in earth axes, is given by:

$$\dot{v}_E^{BE} = T_{EB}\,\dot{v}^{BE} \tag{37}$$

where T_{EB} is the transformation from earth to body axes.

$$T_{EB} = \begin{bmatrix} l_1 & l_2 & l_3 \\ m_1 & m_2 & m_3 \\ n_1 & n_2 & n_3 \end{bmatrix}. \tag{38}$$

l_1, l_2, l_3 are the direction cosines of Ox_E with respect to $O\,x\,y\,z$ and m_1, m_2, m_3 are the direction cosines of Oy_E with respect to $O\,x\,y\,z$.

The velocity in earth axes is:

$$v_E^{BE} = \int \dot{v}_E^{BE}\,dt\,. \tag{39}$$

The displacement in earth axes is:

$$x_E^{BE} = \int v_E^{BE}\,dt\,. \tag{40}$$

The orientation and displacement of two aircraft can be computed relative to the body axes of one of the aircraft. The relative orientation T_{B^*B} of the two body axis systems B^* and B referred to axes B is given by:

$$T_{B^*B} = T_{B^*E} T_{EB} \tag{41}$$

where

$$T_{B^*E} = \begin{bmatrix} l_{1*} & m_{1*} & n_{1*} \\ l_{2*} & m_{2*} & n_{2*} \\ l_{3*} & m_{3*} & n_{3*} \end{bmatrix}. \tag{42}$$

The displacement of each body axis system relative to earth is computed by solving equations (37), (39), (40), for each aircraft. Then the relative displacement in earth axes is:

$$x_E^{B^*B} = x_E^{B^*E} - x_E^{BE}. \tag{43}$$

Then in body axes:

$$x_B^{B^*B} = T_{BE} x_E^{B^*E} \tag{44}$$

Equations (9) and Figure 6.3 give the d.d.a. equations and flow diagram for computing the n direction cosines. The equations for l and m are obtained by writing l and m for n in equations (9). The complete flow diagram comprises three schematics similar to Figure 6.4.

The transformation of the accelerations is achieved by multiplication schematics. For example, the d.d.a. equivalent of equation (37) is:

$$\left. \begin{aligned} d\dot{u}_E &= \dot{u}_o\,dl_1 + l_1\,d\dot{u}_o + \dot{v}_o\,dl_2 + l_2\,d\dot{v}_o + \dot{w}_o\,dl_3 + l_3\,d\dot{w}_o \\ d\dot{v}_E &= \dot{u}_o\,dm_1 + m_1\,d\dot{u}_o + \dot{v}_o\,dm_2 + m_2\,d\dot{v}_o + \dot{w}_o\,dm_3 + m_3\,d\dot{w}_o \\ d\dot{w}_E &= \dot{u}_o\,dn_1 + n_1\,d\dot{u}_o + \dot{v}_o\,dn_2 + n_2\,d\dot{v}_o + \dot{w}_o\,dn_3 + n_3\,d\dot{w}_o. \end{aligned} \right\} \tag{45}$$

The velocities and displacements are obtained by integration schematics. Equation (39) becomes:

$$\left. \begin{aligned} du_E &= \dot{u}_E\,dt \\ dv_E &= \dot{v}_E\,dt \\ dw_E &= \dot{w}_E\,dt. \end{aligned} \right\} \tag{46}$$

Equation (40) becomes:

$$\left. \begin{aligned} dx_E &= u_E\,dt \\ dy_E &= v_E\,dt \\ dz_E &= w_E\,dt. \end{aligned} \right\} \tag{47}$$

As all the transformations require direction cosines their computation is worthy of further study. As the flow diagrams comprise several interconnected loops it may be expected to give rise to errors. If p, q and r are constant the solution for the direction cosines is periodic of period $2\pi/\omega$ where $\omega^2 = p^2 + q^2 + r^2$. Thus the errors with constant rate input can be found by running the computation for n periods and comparing the results during the nth period with those of the first period. For a sequential d.d.a. using a register capacity of 2^{10}, K_t of 2×10^{-3} and p q r of 0.5 rad/sec the maximum error in the 100th period is 68 increments. A check with varying rate inputs can be made by taking p, q and r sinusoidal. If a simple relationship exists between the frequencies of p, q and r the direction cosine solution should again be cyclic. The results during the nth cycle can be compared with those of the first cycle. As expected, the errors are found to be greater than the constant rate case. The ratio of the error to the maximum value of the direction cosine is reduced by increasing the register capacity and the number of increments representing the maximum value, but for a constant K_t this reduces M_p, M_q and M_r.

The reason for the errors becomes apparent when the incremental equations of the computation are studied. Let the subscript n denote conditions at the start of the nth iteration and $n+1$ denote conditions at the start of the $n+1$th iteration, etc.

Then for the general integrator:

$$Y_{n+1} = Y_n + \Delta y_n . \tag{48}$$

The integrator output ΔZ_n at the end of the nth iteration is:

$$\Delta Z_n = Y_{n+1} \Delta x_n . \tag{49}$$

The incremental equations for the nth iteration of the direction cosine equations are therefore:

$$\left.\begin{array}{l} l_{1,n+1} = l_{1,n} + l_{2,n} r_n \Delta t - l_{3,n} q_n \Delta t \\ l_{2,n+1} = l_{2,n} + l_{3,n} p_n \Delta t - l_{1,n} r_n \Delta t \\ l_{3,n+1} = l_{3,n} + l_{1,n} q_n \Delta t - l_{2,n} p_n \Delta t . \end{array}\right\} \tag{50}$$

The change in l during Δt is computed therefore by taking l as constant throughout the time interval Δt. In practice both l and the angular velocities may vary continuously throughout Δt and therefore the computed change is in error.

The errors differ for simultaneous and sequential d.d.a.'s. The simultaneous machine computes the changes in all the direction cosines simultaneously and thus the starting values l_n are taken at the same instant in time. For the sequential machine, by suitable choice of integrators in the iteration cycle, some of the starting values can be taken at time t_n and some at t_{n+1}. This arrangement is found to give significantly less error unless special precautions are taken in the simultaneous machine as discussed in Chapter 7.

A much improved solution is obtained by choosing as the constant values for l the values of l at the mid-point of the time interval Δt. If this value is b_n it can be predicted as:

$$\left. \begin{aligned} b_{1,n} &= l_{1,n} + l_{2,n} r_n \frac{\Delta t}{2} - l_{3,n} q_n \frac{\Delta t}{2} \\[2mm] b_{2,n} &= l_{2,n} + l_{3,n} p_n \frac{\Delta t}{2} - l_{1,n} r_n \frac{\Delta t}{2} \\[2mm] b_{3,n} &= l_{3,n} + l_{1,n} q_n \frac{\Delta t}{2} - l_{2,n} p_n \frac{\Delta t}{2} . \end{aligned} \right\} \tag{51}$$

The value of l at the end of the time interval Δt is therefore given by:

$$\left. \begin{aligned} l_{1,n+1} &= l_{1,n} + b_{2,n} r_n \Delta t - b_{3,n} q_n \Delta t \\ l_{2,n+1} &= l_{2,n} + b_{3,n} p_n \Delta t - b_{1,n} r_n \Delta t \\ l_{3,n+1} &= l_{3,n} + b_{1,n} q_n \Delta t - b_{2,n} p_n \Delta t . \end{aligned} \right\} \tag{52}$$

Thus if the increase in b during $\Delta t/2$ is Δa, the change in b during an iteration is:

$$\left. \begin{aligned} \Delta b_{1,n} &= \Delta l_{1,n+1} + \Delta a_{1,n} - \Delta a_{1,n-1} \\ \Delta b_{2,n} &= \Delta l_{2,n-1} + \Delta a_{2,n} - \Delta a_{2,n-1} \\ \Delta b_{3,n} &= \Delta l_{3,n-1} + \Delta a_{3,n} - \Delta a_{3,n-1} . \end{aligned} \right\} \tag{53}$$

The flow diagram for solving equations (51), (52), (53) on a sequential d.d.a. is shown by Figure 6.5. The integrator outputs for the nth iteration are given. The order of integrators in the machine cycle is (s, l, b, a). The capacity of integrators (l) is twice that of (b) in order to perform the divide-by-two operation. As adders (s) are processed before (l) in the iteration period the Δa increments passed from (s) to (b) are delayed by one iteration period with a change of sign. Integrators (b) have ΔY inputs from (l, s, a) thus satisfying equation (53). In order to avoid errors being produced when adders (s) receive inputs from integrators (l) at the same time, the Δt inputs to the integrators producing the angular velocity terms $p_n \Delta t$, $q_n \Delta t$, $r_n \Delta t$, must not exceed half machine rate.

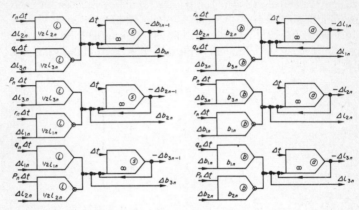

Figure 6.5. *Corrected direction cosine program.*

In the case of a simultaneous d.d.a. the iteration period is spread over two machine cycles. In the first, the adders (s) have Δt inputs and integrators $(l)p_n\Delta t$ inputs, thus preparing the Δb_n inputs. In the second machine cycle, (b, a) receive $p_n\Delta t$ and Δt inputs respectively. Thus equations (51), (52), (53) are processed in the correct order.

The program of Figure 6.5 has been run on a sequential d.d.a. and found to give excellent results. The errors are insignificant for the length of computation normally required. This improvement in accuracy is gained at the expense of doubling the number of integrators.

6.8 Improvements to the representation of the aerodynamics

The programs outlined in 6.4 assumed the stability derivatives to be constant. This assumption is only valid for small changes of aircraft motion relative to the reference flight condition. In particular, very large changes of the derivatives can occur in the transonic regime. For more realistic simulations at least the more important derivatives must therefore be variable.

The generation of arbitrary functions is not easily carried out by the d.d.a., generally requiring large numbers of integrators. The methods outlined in

Chapter 3 require too many integrators for application to this simulation exercise. Additional logic must therefore be provided to generate variable derivatives.

With simultaneous d.d.a.'s of the type discussed in Chapter 7 such units may be provided which store values of a function and the intervals of the independent variable for which these values apply. The values may be transferred from the store to the Y register of an integrator and the units controlled by incremental inputs of the independent variables. Such a system can represent the derivatives in two ways. The stored numbers may be values of a derivative, for example Z_u/m and the range of u for which each value shall apply. This method requires one integrator per derivative. A second and more accurate method is to store values $(d/du)(Zu/m)$ and the ranges of u for which each value shall apply. The aerodynamic contribution of Z_u is computed as:

$$d\left(\frac{uZ_u}{m}\right) = \frac{Z_u}{m}\,du + u\,d\left(\frac{Z_u}{m}\right) \tag{54}$$

where:

$$d\left(\frac{Z_u}{m}\right) = \frac{d}{du}\left(\frac{Z_u}{m}\right)du. \tag{55}$$

The flow diagram for this form of representation as shown in Figure 6.6

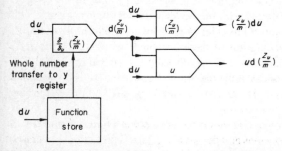

Figure 6.6. Representing a derivative using a function store.

requires three integrators per derivative. For a given simulation both methods could be used, the second for the derivatives providing the major contributions to the aerodynamics.

6.9 The integrated wind tunnel—flight dynamic simulator

The major parts of the aerodynamic forces and moments are provided by the static derivatives, i.e. the derivatives with respect to u, v, w, and control angles. These derivatives are generally calculated from the results of wind tunnel measurements. This suggests that a wind tunnel could be used as a function generator for the static aerodynamics passing data directly to an on-line computer controlling the orientation of the model in the tunnel. This system eliminates the errors arising from the reduction of the measured aerodynamic data to derivatives and subsequent regeneration of the aerodynamics by the computer.

In a system employing this principle [3] the six force and moment components are measured on a model in a wind tunnel and passed to on-line computers which solve the equations of motion of the vehicle. The resulting velocity components u, v, w, are used to orientate the model to the tunnel wind and the resultant velocity V used to control the tunnel windspeed.

As the model is continuously in motion in the tunnel its inertia will produce inertial forces and torques which may be detected by the balance system and interpreted as aerodynamic forces and moments. To prevent this having any effect on the simulation the acceleration of the model must be limited so that the inertial loads are less than the sensitivity of the balance. This can be achieved by running the simulation slower than real time. For a typical Mach-2 missile simulation the time scale extension will be of the order of $50:1$, which results in the measured aerodynamic loads due to angular velocity, accelerations and control angular rates, being insignificant. Even in real time the model representation of these contributions would be incorrect owing to the scaling laws between the full-scale aircraft and the model. The tunnel therefore generates only the static aerodynamics. The remaining aerodynamic contributions are usually small and may be represented by derivatives with sufficient accuracy.

The aerodynamic forces and moments measured in a tunnel are presented as voltages or shaft positions and passed to a d.d.a. via an analogue to digital converter converting volts or shaft position to either digital whole numbers X_T, Y_T, Z_T, L_T, M_T, N_T or increments ΔX_T, ΔY_T, ΔZ_T, ΔL_T, ΔM_T, ΔN_T. The equations representing the forces and moments in the computer then become:

$$\left.\begin{aligned}
X &= X_T + T_X \\
Y &= Y_T + pY_p + rY_r + T_y \\
Z &= Z_T + \dot{w}Z_{\dot{w}} + qZ_q + T_z
\end{aligned}\right\} \tag{56}$$

$$L = L_T + pL_p + rL_r + \dot{\xi}L_{\dot{\xi}}$$
$$M = M_T + \dot{w}M_{\dot{w}} + qM_q + \dot{\eta}M_{\dot{\eta}} + R_y$$
$$N = N_T + \dot{v}N_{\dot{v}} + pN_p + rN_r + \dot{\zeta}N_{\dot{\zeta}} .$$

(57)

The solution of the equations of motion follows the methods outlined in 6.4. If the analogue-to-digital conversion system gives incremental inputs the equations can be solved to give accelerations, but if only whole number inputs are available the solution will give velocities.

The resulting velocity components are used to position the model in the tunnel. The model orientation to the wind can be defined by two angles α and β:

$$\sin \alpha = w/V \tag{58}$$
$$\sin \beta = v/V. \tag{59}$$

These angles are set by the mechanical model support system and the equations solved by the methods outlined in Chapter 3. The quotients present no difficulty as V is always large. The program time scale extension must be such that the maximum demanded values of $\ddot{\alpha}$ and $\ddot{\beta}$ (with respect to real time) do not cause detectable inertia leads on the balance.

An alternative support system often used for supersonic wind tunnels uses polar co-ordinares, where the orientation of the model to the wind is defined by a resultant incidence σ in a fixed plane, usually vertical in the tunnel, and a rotation λ of the model relative to the incidence plane. Thus:

$$\sin \sigma = \frac{(v^2 + w^2)^{\frac{1}{2}}}{V} \tag{60}$$

$$\tan \lambda = v/w. \tag{61}$$

These are more conveniently expressed as:

$$\sin \sigma = (\bar{v}^2 + \bar{w}^2)^{\frac{1}{2}} \tag{62}$$
$$\tan \lambda = \bar{v}/\bar{w} \tag{63}$$

where $\bar{v} = v/w$, $\bar{w} = w/V$.

The equations cannot be solved in this form. When $\bar{w}$ approaches zero, $\tan \lambda$ tends to infinity and therefore cannot be represented by the d.d.a. Where $\bar{v}$ and $\bar{w}$ are simultaneously small the computation of sine by the square root program is inaccurate.

Equation (63) can be rewritten as:

$$\bar{w} \sin \lambda - \bar{v} \cos \lambda = 0 . \tag{64}$$

In differential form this becomes:

$$\bar{w} \cos \lambda \, d\lambda + \sin \lambda \, d\bar{w} + \bar{v} \sin \lambda \, d\lambda - \cos \lambda \, d\lambda = 0 . \tag{65}$$

This equation can be solved by a servo program. The servo active element produces $d\lambda$ increments to drive a sine/cosine loop. The servo output, which is either full machine rate or zero is not ideally suited as an input to the model support mechanism.

The servo equation is easily converted to an Amble equation

$$\sin \lambda \, d\bar{w} - \cos \lambda \, d\bar{v} + (\bar{w} \cos \lambda + \bar{v} \sin \lambda - 1) d\lambda = -d\lambda \tag{66}$$

$$\sin \lambda \, d\bar{w} - \cos \lambda \, d\bar{v} + [(\textstyle\int \cos \lambda \, d\bar{w} + \sin \lambda \, d\bar{v}$$
$$- \bar{w} \sin \lambda \, d\lambda + \bar{v} \cos \lambda \, d\lambda) - 1] \, d\lambda = -d\lambda . \tag{67}$$

This equation is solved by the flow diagram of Figure 6.7.

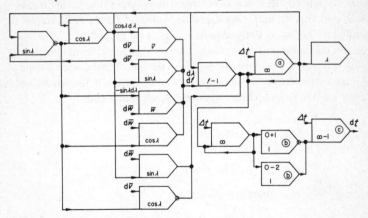

Figure 6.7. Amble computation of λ.

The Amble program provides a continuously varying output rate and therefore gives a smoother input to the model support mechanism.

As $\bar{w}$ becomes small λ can tend to infinity, since:

$$\dot{\lambda} = \frac{\bar{w}\dot{\bar{v}} - \bar{v}\dot{\bar{w}}}{\bar{w}^2} \tag{68}$$

The λ attainable in the computer is limited to that represented by $d\lambda$ increments at full machine rate. An excessive demand for λ causes error increments to accumulate in the Y register of the servo active element. These error increments are summed by an adder, the output of which is passed to a limit switch. The limit switch gives an output increment when the error exceeds $\pm e$ increments. This increment is used to inhibit the input of problem time, dt, increments to the simulation. This stops computation of $\bar{v}$ and $\bar{w}$ allowing the error to decrease. The switching on and off of the time input occurs at very high frequency and the simulation can be regarded as being carried out on a variable time scale.

In the case of the Amble program, demand for an excessive λ causes increments to accumulate in the Y register of the adder. This accumulation is summed and used to operate a limit switch (integrators (b) of Figure 6.7) which controls the time input dt to the simulation.

If λ is known σ can be computed from:

$$\sin \sigma = \bar{w} \cos \lambda + \bar{v} \sin \lambda \qquad (69)$$

In differential form:

$$d(\sin \sigma) = -\bar{w} \sin \lambda d\lambda + \cos \lambda d\bar{w} + \bar{v} \cos \lambda d\lambda + \sin \lambda d\bar{v}. \qquad (70)$$

σ is computed by the normal Amble method. As $\dot{\sigma}$ is of the same order as $\bar{\dot{v}}$ and $\bar{\dot{w}}$ this computation present no problems.

The maximum values of the derivatives $\dot{\sigma}$, λ and $\ddot{\sigma}$ with respect to real time which can be allowed in the tunnel are limited partly by the need to restrict inertia loads on the model and partly by the mechanical limitations of the model support system. The computer program must be controlled so that these tunnel limitations are not exceeded. The maximum values of $\dot{\sigma}$ and λ that can be demanded by the computer are IK_σ and IK_λ. The values of the scale constants K_σ and K_λ are dependent on K_t, therefore the tunnel limitations on $\dot{\sigma}$ and λ govern K_t. The variation of the time input to the simulation produced by the computation of λ extends the time scale beyond the value IK_t which is produced by full machine rate time increment input.

Unless $\bar{v}$ and $\bar{w}$ are identically zero, σ will never be zero and will be confined to either positive or negative values. Thus the direction of change of σ may have to be rapidly reversed when σ is small producing large $\ddot{\sigma}$ demands. This would produce inertia loads detectable by the balance.

If at incidence σ_c the model has velocity $\dot{\sigma}_c$ and is to be decelerated sinusoidally to rest at $\sigma = 0$, then during the subsequent motion

$$\sigma = \sigma_c \sin nt \tag{71}$$

$$\dot{\sigma} = n\sigma_c \cos nt \tag{72}$$

$$\ddot{\sigma} = -n^2 \sigma_c \sin nt \tag{73}$$

where n is a constant and t is real time.

Thus: $$n = \dot{\sigma}_c/\sigma_c \tag{74}$$

and the maximum acceleration $\ddot{\sigma}_m$ is:

$$\ddot{\sigma}_m = -\dot{\sigma}_c^2/\sigma_c. \tag{75}$$

Thus the acceleration which can be demanded increases as $1/\sigma_c$.

If at incidence σ_c the time increment input rate is decreased by a factor $(h\sigma_c)^{\frac{1}{2}}$ where h is a constant, the time scale is further extended locally by $1/(h\sigma_c)^{\frac{1}{2}}$, then the maximum acceleration becomes:

$$\ddot{\sigma}_m = \frac{-[\dot{\sigma}_c(h\sigma_c)^{\frac{1}{2}}]^2}{\sigma_{c2}} \tag{76}$$

therefore $$\ddot{\sigma} = h(\dot{\sigma}_c). \tag{77}$$

Since $\sigma_c \leqslant IK_\sigma$, suitable choice of h would ensure that the $\ddot{\sigma}$ limitation was not exceeded. However, the computation of the square root is unreliable at small values of σ_c and therefore a less suitable time scale extension law must be adapted. A linear law extending the time scale by $1/h_1 \sigma_c$ is permissible. Then:

$$\ddot{\sigma}_m = h_1^2 \sigma_c \dot{\sigma}_c^2. \tag{78}$$

To avoid the computation stopping at $\sigma = 0$ the minimum value of σ_c is taken as being the discrimination of the computation, i.e. K_σ. Thus the maximum time scale extension produced by this law is $1/h_1 K_\sigma$.

As change of λ is affected by rolling the model about its Ox axis, the inertial loads produced by $\ddot{\lambda}$ are very small. No special precautions need be taken to control $\ddot{\lambda}$ as the $\dot{\lambda}$ and $\ddot{\sigma}$ limitations will ensure that no large values of $\ddot{\lambda}$ are demanded.

The local time scale of the simulation will be determined by the cumulative effects of K_t and the time scale extensions due to the $\dot{\lambda}$ and $\ddot{\sigma}$ limitations.

6.10 The advantages of a d.d.a. simulation

The d.d.a. in general can provide more accurate results as it can readily carry out the extensive amount of multiplication necessary in the solution of the equations of the simulation. These provide great difficulties for analogue computers as the accuracy of analogue servo/multipliers is generally less than 0·1 per cent. However, with current d.d.a.'s this accuracy is achieved at a much slower solution rate. A d.d.a. of the type described in Chapter 7 can provide a representation of 0·01 per cent at about 0·1 c/s. A real time missile simulation may produce frequencies of 10 c/s, a frequency easily attainable with analogue machines. D.d.a. simulations therefore have to be carried out on an extended time scale. However, developments in solid-state logic elements suggest that real time computing with a representation of at least 0·1 per cent will be achieved in the future.

References

[1] ETKIN, B. *Dynamics of Flight*, John Wiley, N.Y.

[2] THOMAS, H. H. B. M. (August 1961) 'Estimation of Stability Derivatives' *ARC Current Paper* 664

[3] BEECHAM, L. J., WALTERS, W. L. and PARTRIDGE, D. W. 'Proposals for an Integrated Wind Tunnel—Flight Dynamics Simulator' *ARC Current Paper* 789.

7: The Simultaneous D.D.A.

7.1 Choice of integration law for the simultaneous integrator

In Chapter 2, the design of a basic digital integrator is described and the general form of the simultaneous type of d.d.a. is outlined. In this chapter the special considerations involved in designing a simultaneous d.d.a. are discussed in detail and broad specifications are derived for units which can be used to build up a computer of this type.

It is apparent from Chapter 4 that the simultaneous type of d.d.a. organization gives rise to larger errors than does the sequential and greater care is needed, therefore, when designing a simultaneous machine to make the errors insignificant. It is instructive to tabulate the successive values of sin θ and cos θ as generated by a pair of simultaneous digital integrators for various integration laws. If the suffix n is used to represent the present value of a quantity, and $n+1$ its new value, we can write:

$$R_{n+1} = R_n + Y_n \tag{1}$$

for the operation in the R register, and

$$Y_{n+1} = Y_n + \mathrm{d}y_n \tag{2}$$

for the operation in the Y register. Suppose, now, that the capacity of the Y and R registers is one decimal digit and that two integrators operating according to the above integration law are connected in a sine-cosine loop, then the successive values of sin θ and cos θ are as shown in Table 7.1. The first row associated with a value of θ corresponds to the operation on the R register expressed in equation (1) and the second row, the operation of equation (2) upon the Y register.

It can be seen that after step 16, corresponding to a value of 1·6 radians, the value of cos θ has fallen to zero, as expected, but the value of sin θ has increased to 10, instead of the correct value of 8, despite the fact that the R register was initially set half-full to give the optimum conditions. The results are shown in Figure 7.1 in which sin θ is plotted against θ, the continuous line giving the true value of sin θ.

142

Table 7.1

θ	cos θ			sin θ		
	Y	R	dz	Y	R	dz
0	8	5	0	0	5	0
0·1	8	3	1	0	5	0
	8		0	1		0
0·2	8	1	1	1	5	0
	8	.	0	2		0
0·3	8	9	0	2	6	0
	8		0	2		0
0·4	8	7	1	2	8	0
	8		0	3		0
0·5	8	5	1	3	0	1
	7		0	4		0
0·6	7	3	1	4	3	0
	7		0	5		0
0 7	7	0	1	5	7	0
	7		0	6		0
0·8	7	7	0	6	2	1
	6		0	6		0
0·9	6	4	1	6	8	0
	6		0	7		0
1·0	6	0	1	7	4	1
	5		0	8		0
1·1	5	6	0	8	1	1
	4		0	8		0
1·2	4	1	1	8	9	0
	4		0	9		0
1·3	4	5	0	9	7	1
	3		0	9		0
1·4	3	9	0	9	6	1
	2		0	9		0
1·5	2	2	1	9	5	1
	1		0	10		0
1·6	1	4	0	10	4	1
	0		0	10		0
1·7	0	5	0	10	4	1
	−1		0	10		0

An alternative integration law can be used in which the new value in the Y register, Y_{n+1}, is used to form the new value in the R register, R_{n+1}. The integration law then becomes:

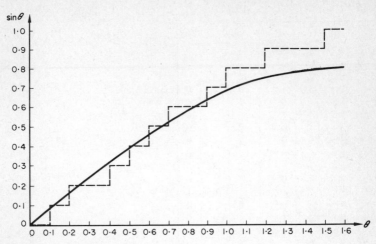

Figure 7.1. The sin θ/θ curve.

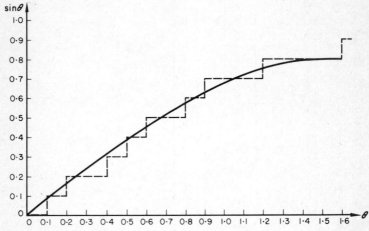

Figure 7.2. The sin θ/θ curve with a different integration law.

$$R_{n+1} = R_n + Y_{n+1} \tag{3}$$

$$Y_{n+1} = Y_n + \mathrm{d}y_n. \tag{4}$$

An alternative form of equation (3) is:

$$R_{n+1} = R_n + Y_n + \mathrm{d}y_n. \tag{5}$$

Table 7.2

θ	cos θ			sin θ		
	Y	R	dz	Y	R	dz
0	8	5	0	0	5	0
0·1	8	3	1	0	5	0
	8		0	1		0
0·2	8	1	1	1	6	0
	8		0	2		0
0·3	8	9	0	2	8	0
	8		0	2		0
0·4	8	7	1	2	0	1
	7		0	3		0
0·5	7	4	1	3	3	0
	7		0	4		0
0·6	7	1	1	4	7	0
	7		0	5		0
0 7	7	0	0	5	2	1
	6		0	5		0
0·8	6	4	1	5	7	0
	6		0	6		0
0 9	6	0	1	6	3	1
	5		0	7		0
1·0	5	5	0	7	0	1
	4		0	7		0
1·1	4	9	0	7	7	0
	4		0	7		0
1·2	4	3	1	7	4	1
	3		0	8		0
1·3	3	6	0	8	2	1
	2		0	8		0
1·4	2	8	0	8	0	1
	1		0	8		0
1·5	1	0	1	8	8	0
	1		0	9		0
1·6	1	1	0	9	7	1
	0		0	9		0
1·7	0	1	0	9	6	1
	−1		0	9		0

The result of using the law in the single decimal digit integrator is given in Table 7.2 and Figure 7.2. The error is smaller than before but the correct amplitude of the function is still not retained. If sin θ is plotted against cos θ, as shown in Figure 7.3, the spiralling outwards of the circle can be seen clearly. Whilst it is uncommon in problems for the value of θ in a sin-cosine loop to exceed the range 0 to 2π radians, the effect of the error in a more complex combination of integrators may be significant for a smaller range of values of

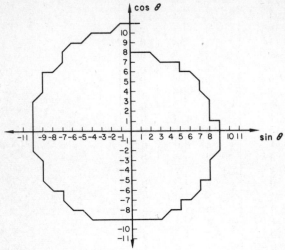

Figure 7.3. *Sin θ vs. cos θ.*

the variable of integration and it is very desirable that the operation of the integrator be as good as possible.

Consider now the effect of an increment in θ on the cosine function. Expanding trigonometrically:

$$\cos(\theta + d\theta) = \cos\theta\cos d\theta - \sin\theta\sin d\theta$$

$$= \cos\theta\left(1 - \frac{(d\theta)^2}{2!} + \frac{(d\theta)^4}{4!} - \cdots\right)$$

$$- \sin\theta\left(d\theta - \frac{(d\theta)^3}{3!} + \cdots\right).$$

Ignoring third and higher powers of $d\theta$:

$$\cos(\theta + d\theta) = \cos\theta - \sin\theta\, d\theta - \frac{(d\theta)^2}{2}\cos\theta. \qquad (6)$$

The first two terms on the right-hand side of equation (6) are those which are operative in the design of integrator so far discussed. The new value of cos θ is formed by subtracting the increments in the integral formed in the other integrator, these being generated by the product of the contents of its Y register (sin θ) and the increment in the variable of integration, $(d\theta)$. In order to obtain an improvement in the accuracy of the integrator it is necessary to

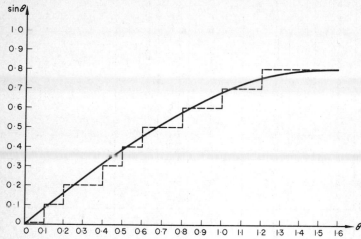

Figure 7.4. The sin θ/θ curve with stable radius.

make arrangements to include the third term and, thereby, the second-order terms in the expansion. If this is rewritten:

$$\frac{(d\theta)^2}{2} \cos \theta = \frac{d\theta}{2} \cos \theta \, d\theta$$

$$= \frac{d\theta}{2} \, d(\sin \theta)$$

then it follows that the necessary extra term can be generated by multiplying any increment in sin θ by half the increment in the variable of integration. Expressing this in the form of an integration law, results in the revised form:

$$R_{n+1} = R_n + Y_{n+1} + \tfrac{1}{2} dy_n \, d\theta_n \tag{7}$$

$$Y_{n+1} = Y_n + dy_n . \tag{8}$$

The effect of this law upon the single decimal digit computation of sin θ and cos θ is shown in Table 7.3 and Figure 7.4.

Table 7.3

θ	cos θ			sin θ		
	Y	R	dz	Y	R	dz
0	8	5	0	0	5	0
0·1	8	3	1	0	5	0
	8		0	1	5·5	0
0·2	8	1	1	1	6·5	0
	8		0	2	7	0
0·3	8	9	0	2	9	0
	8		0	2		0
0·4	8	7	1	2	1	1
	7	6·5	0	3	1·5	0
0·5	7	3·5	1	3	4·5	0
	7		0	4	5	0
0·6	7	0·5	1	4	9	0
	7		0	5	9·5	0
0·7	7	7·5	0	5	4·5	1
	6	7	0	5		0
0·8	6	3	1	5	9·5	0
	6		0	6	0	1
0·9	6	9	0	6	6	1
	5	8·5	0	6		0
1·0	5	3·5	1	6	2	1
	4	3	0	7	2·5	0
1·1	4	7	0	7	9·5	0
	4		0	7		0
1·2	4	1	1	7	6·5	1
	3	0·5	0	8	7	0
1·3	3	3·5	0	8	5	1
	2	3	0	8		0
1·4	2	5	0	8	3	1
	1	4·5	0	8		0
1·5	1	5·5	0	8	1	1
	0	5	0	8		0
1·6	0	5	0	8	9	0
	0	5	0	8		0
1·7	0	5	0	8	7	1
	−1	4·5	0	8		0

For convenience in setting out the operation the addition, or subtraction, of the extra term has been included in the first line of each pair and the addition of any increment to the value of Y only shown in the second. In step number 8 it will be seen that the addition of the extra term produces a dz signal which is then fed to the other integrator at the succeeding dz time. Such a situation can arise in a practical integrator and for this provision has to be made. Two dz increments can never be generated in one integration step, however, since the addition of the extra term only adds one half in the least significant place of the R register and this, added even to the contents of a full Y register, cannot exceed the R register capacity. It is seen from Table 7.3 and Figure 7.4 that the radius of the circle has remained stable and, in fact, this remains so regardless of the number of times the circle is gone round. This integration method is known as the trapezoidal law since its effect is to add the area of a trapezium into the R register.

The remaining type of error, which has already been mentioned, is that caused by reversals in the variable of integration. This effect can be simply demonstrated in terms of the single decimal digit integrator. The steady drift in the contents of the R register is present with all the integration laws so far described, including the trapezoidal law, as shown in Table 7.4.

Table 7.4

dx	dy	Y	R	dz
		5	5	0
	+	6	5·5	
+		6	1·5	+1
	−	5	1	
−		5	6	−1
	+	6	6·5	
+		6	2·5	+1
	−	5	2	
−		5	7	−1

In large-scale problems, involving many interconnected integrators, the situation can easily arise where reversals in a variable of integration occur. Clearly, it is vital that this drift effect is eliminated from the integrator by suitable design, otherwise appreciable errors may occur in problem solutions. Considering the pair of integrators connected in a sine-cosine loop, as shown in Figure 7.5, a dθ signal will cause the contents of the Y registers in both integrators to be added simultaneously to their associated R registers and possibly increments in the integral to be emitted. If the trapezoidal law is used, then the new value in the R register is given by:

$$R_{n+1} = R_n + (\sin \theta)_{n+1} + \tfrac{1}{2}\mathrm{d}\theta_n \mathrm{d}(\sin \theta)_n.$$

Now the last term in this expression is the second-order term and the $\mathrm{d}(\sin \theta)$ factor was generated by the *previous* $\mathrm{d}\theta$ signal. Strictly speaking, therefore, the correct form of the equation should be:

$$R_{n+1} = R_n + (\sin \theta)_{n+1}\,\mathrm{d}\theta_n + \tfrac{1}{2}\mathrm{d}\theta_{n-1}\,\mathrm{d}(\sin \theta)_n. \qquad (9)$$

In other words, the second-order term should be generated by the product of any increment in $\sin \theta$ and the previous value of $\mathrm{d}\theta$. It is the failure to take account of the time lag naturally inherent in the digital integrator which causes reversals to give rise to the drift in the R register. If the correct second-order term is generated as given in equation (9), then this error is eliminated as illustrated in Table 7.5, which shows the same situation as given in Table 7.4, but employing the amended term.

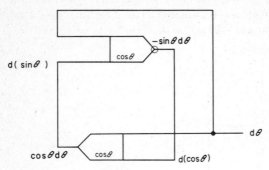

Figure 7.5. The sin θ/cosine θ loop.

Table 7.5

dx	dy	Y	R	dz
		5	5	0
	+	6	4·5	
+		6	0·5	+1
	−	5	0	
−		5	5	−1
	+	6	4·5	
+		6	0·5	+1
	−	5	0	
−		5	5	−1

So far, the sin-cosine loop has been used to illustrate the types of errors encountered in a simultaneous digital integrator. The use of the trapezoidal law and the previous value of dx for forming the second-order term can, however, be justified on more general grounds. Consider the Taylor expansion:

$$f(x+dx) = f(x) + f'(x)dx + \frac{f''(x)}{2!}(dx)^2 + \dots .$$

As many terms of this expansion can be taken as are required to provide the required precision in a digital integrator, provided that it is remembered that the value of dx required in a given term is one which caused the generation of the remainder of the term. In other words, the expression is:

$$f(x+dx) = f(x) + f'(x)dx_n + \frac{f''(x)}{2!}(dx_{n-1})^2 + \frac{f'''(x)}{3!}(dx_{n-2})^3 + \dots . \quad (10)$$

In practice, the realization of a corrected integrator which takes account of previous values of dx involves extra complexity to store these values and to employ them, so that such steps are only taken where necessary.

7.2 Functional facilities

Consider a differential equation of the form:

$$dy = x^2 dx + kx dy + f(x)dx$$
$$\text{for } 0.5 \leqslant x \leqslant 1.5$$

For $x < 0.5$, $dy = kx dy$.

For $x > 1.5$, $dy = x^2 dx$.

The first term on the right-hand side of the basic equation requires straightforward integration of x^2 with respect to x. The second term involves the multiplication of an integral by the constant k, and the third involves the generation of an arbitrary function of x. These three terms have to be added together to form dy, and finally, the form of the equation is a function of the value of x, and certain terms have to be eliminated if the value of x goes outside prescribed limits. These requirements are typical of those required in simulation of physical systems by mathematical models on a d.d.a. The required functional operations are, therefore:

(i) integration,

(ii) multiplication by a coefficient,
(iii) addition of terms,
(iv) function generation,
(v) decision making and switching.
Each of these are now discussed in more detail.

7.2.1 *Integration*

The method of integration to be preferred for use in an integrator in a simultaneous d.d.a. has already been discussed at some length from the point of view of the integration law to be used. Other facilities are needed to make it possible to use an integrator to solve differential equations, however. The first of these is that of setting in the initial conditions of the problem. This involves clearing the Y register of any number it already contains and replacing it by the required initial value. Some means of associating a given value with a particular integrator is also necessary. It is often desirable to be able to repeat the solution of a problem with one parameter slightly changed to try out the effect of this on the solution, and in these circumstances it is vital that the initial values can be set quickly and easily. To do this implies storage of these values in a form which allows them to be inserted into the Y registers quickly, on demand.

One of the properties of the d.d.a. already mentioned is that of the interchange of precision for speed of integration. If the operating precision of an integrator can be reduced n times, then the speed of response can be increased by the same factor n. In some problems, closed loops of integrators are found which simulate a low precision, fast response part of a system but within a larger assembly of units simulating a much slower part of the system with a greater required precision. In these cases, it is convenient to be able to vary the precision of individual integrators and to gain a localized increase in speed. This facility can readily be provided by a scaling factor on the dy input to the Y register. Instead of feeding an increment, dy, in y direct to the Y register, it can be used to control a gate which allows a predetermined number to be added instead. The range of scaling can be made as wide as desired by merely providing a greater number of values under control of a selection device, such as a multi-position switch.

The two facilities just mentioned are essential if a digital integrator is to be used effectively in a simultaneous d.d.a. Other facilities, however, can be provided to make it easier to operate. One of these is means of monitoring the present value in the Y register. When running a problem, it is often desirable, and indeed essential, to be able to see how a particular variable is changing. It may also be desirable to take a permanent record of the variable during the course of the computation on a print-out device, punched paper tape, or on a plotting table. Access needs to be provided, therefore, to the Y register to allow its contents to be available to various devices external to the integrator itself.

Another useful facility is that of detecting when the value of y is approaching the maximum capacity of the Y register. This is similar to the overload detection on analogue operational amplifiers, and provides a check on the scaling of the problem. This can be provided by continuously comparing the contents of the Y register with a preset number built into the integrator and sending out an alarm signal when this is exceeded. Unlike the analogue differential analyser, it is feasible to stop the computer completely when this happens without loss of accuracy so that the various values can be checked to find out what has gone wrong.

7.2.2 *Coefficient multiplication*

Coefficient multiplication is equivalent to integration of a constant with respect to the variable of integration. It is perfectly feasible, therefore, to use an integrator set with the value of the coefficient as the initial condition and with no dy input signals. Alternatively, a special type of logic may be devised for this purpose. Whilst the scaling facility already mentioned in connexion with the integrator could be used to provide scaling by a coefficient, it would be an expensive complication of each integrator to provide the complete range of scaling factors from the smallest possible to the largest possible number represented within an integrator. Anything less comprehensive then this is inadequate. For a special purpose machine, intended to solve one fixed set of differential equations, the use of a specially designed set of logic is usually more economical then using integrators as coefficient multipliers. Quite often, the problem can be scaled in such a way that the number of coefficients is reduced, or so that some of them are transformed into binary powers, which can be easily provided. In the general case, however, the number of coefficient units required will vary widely from problem to problem.

In a general purpose simultaneous d.d.a., therefore, it is preferable to design the integrator in such a way that it is possible to use it either as an integrator, or as a coefficient multiplier. Since the necessary facilities are already required in the integrator there is no penalty in doing this except that, for a given problem, the combination of integrators and coefficient multipliers costs more than would otherwise be necessary for the solution of that particular problem. However, considering the equipment as a whole, because of their interchangeability, the total number of units could be reduced from that required if separate integrators and coefficient multipliers were individually provided to deal with the most complex problem to be expected.

7.2.3 *Addition of pulse rates*

Addition of trains of dz pulses coming from integrators and coefficient multiplier outputs is frequently required to form a single quantity for augmenting a value of y as a dx input to an integrator. There are two distinct ways of looking at this requirement. One is to regard the sum as meaning that n units of dy need to be added to the receiving Y register when n increments are present simultaneously and are to be added together. This is perfectly adequate for increments in an integrand but when the sum is required to be used as a variable of integration it is not possible to increase the size of the step in the variable of integration and the sum must, in fact, be taken as a number of individual steps. This suggests that what is needed is an adding device which will produce a train of pulses whose output pulse rate is the sum of the input pulse rates. Since the pulse rates within a d.d.a. provide an equally good representation of the quantities concerned as do the values in the Y registers, this approach is perfectly justified and results in a much simpler design of adding logic.

If a single increment arrived at one of the inputs of such an adder it would appear at the output forthwith. If two increments arrived simultaneously, then one of these would be fed out and the other stored until the next output pulse time and then emitted. This principle can be extended to as many input pulse rates must not exceed the maximum rate at which increments can be transmitted around the machine.

If this method is adopted, then the question of the effect of delays to increments arises again. As described in Section 1, any delays introduced between one integrator and another may cause an increment in an integrand to be separated from the increment in the variable of integration which generated it.

The situation when an adder is combining a number of sources of increments to form a combined source of increments in an integrand is a complex one which varies from problem to problem. It is no longer possible to associate a particular increment with a particular variable of integration increment since this is a function of the pattern of pulses arriving at the adder input as well as of the pattern of units required to solve the problem. Fortunately, errors will only arise due to reversals in the variable of integration and these are not always present. If they are, it is found in practice that an integrator with the improved trapezoidal law which takes account of delays gives good accuracy even if an adder is involved and that this problem is not a serious one. If the adder is summing pulses to form a variable of integration, a similar situation arises, except that in this case the delay of such an increment is equivalent to advancing the increments in an integrand with respect to the variable of integration. This tends to cancel out errors due to reversals in some cases but not in others. As for the summation of increments in the integrand, it is found in practice that errors due to summation are not serious. If reversals are likely at the output of an adder feeding a dx input, however, it has been found preferable to use a corrected integrator rather than an uncorrected one.

Analysis of the frequency distribution of numbers of inputs to summing units required against the number of times these are fully used shows that the number of times a high number of inputs is required is very small. Most problems are satisfied with not more than seven inputs and if this is not sufficient it is always possible to place adders in tandem.

Useful additional facilities for an adder are an overload warning which indicates when the sum of the input pulse rates exceeds the maximum increment pulse rate. This can be arranged to stop the computation, if required. A further useful refinement is to have a multiplying factor switch which divides the pulse rate by a preset constant. This allows the sum of the input pulse rates to exceed the machine maximum rate and also provides some scaling which avoids the use of coefficient multipliers in some cases.

7.2.4 *Function generation*

In an analogue computer, integration is only possible with respect to one variable of integration – time. The ability of the d.d.a. to integrate with respect to any quantity represented within it means that many functions which, in an analogue computer would have to be generated by means of a function generator, can be generated in the d.d.a. from their definitive differential equations. As is shown in Chapter 3 all trigonometric functions, for example, can be generated from combinations of integrators and adders. Function generators are only required in a d.d.a. for the generation of truly arbitrary functions, therefore, and as these are usually the results of experiments, they are not normally known to great precision and a function generator for use in the type of d.d.a. being considered here need not be of greater precision than the original data. This fact can be used to simplify the design.

The data specifying the arbitrary function will normally be available in the form of a number of pairs of ordinates, rather than as a smooth curve. Ideally, the d.d.a. should accept the data in this form as an input to the function generator which then generates the required function by some interpolation method for values between the specified points. Owing to the relatively low precision of the data as compared with the precision of the d.d.a. it is usually adequate to use straight-line interpolation, particularly if the points can be arranged to be specified anywhere in the range of the function, rather than at predetermined fixed intervals. A part of the function with a high curvature can then be specified with a larger number of points than a less highly curved part, always providing, of course, that control of the generation of the experimental points is possible. If this is not so, then a smooth curve can always be plotted from the available data and a suitable set of co-ordinate pairs selected for feeding to the function generator.

The requirement, therefore, is for a linear interpolator in association with a store which holds the pairs of points which specify the function. It has already been observed that the integrator can be used for multiplication by a constant and providing that the slope of the straight line between each pair of points on the approximation to the arbitrary function is known, then this can be used in the Y register of an integrator to form the approximation to $f(x)dx$ if dx increments are fed to the dx input of the integrator.

The design of a unit to calculate the slopes of the straight lines would be relatively expensive and probably cannot normally be justified, particularly when it is remembered that arbitrary functions are likely to be used many times, once they have been generated. There is little objection, in such cases, to preparing a graph of the arbitrary function, to choosing the ordinates in an optimum manner to give a good fit of the approximation to the function and to measuring the slopes of the straight lines representing the function between the chosen points. The arbitrary function generator can, therefore, consist of a store which holds the values of the independent variable at which the slope of the approximation changes together with the slope of the straight line to one side of the turning point, an integrator to form the product $f(x)dx$, and a control part which keeps track of the value of x and causes a new slope to be fed to the Y register of the integrator when a turning point is reached.

If the function unit is organized in this way, a further advantage is obtained in that a function $f(x)dy$ can be generated by feeding increments in x to the control part and increments in y to the integrator. A function of two variables can thus be generated by forming $f(x)dy+f(y)dx$, and this principle can be extended to deal with functions of several variables, if required.

Preferably, means should be available for the values of the slopes of the straight lines and the values of x at which there are turning points to be inserted into the store easily. This then allows a machine to be used for a number of different problems with the minimum of time for setting up.

The scheme outlined above provides a flexible digital function generator whose precision can be made to match the precision of the available data quite closely. It is, however, a fairly complex kind of unit to realize in practice and where the arbitrary function is not known to more than a precision of a few per cent, a simpler approach is possible. A cathode-ray tube with a mask representing the function can be employed, with a photocell to servo the c.r.t. spot on to the line of the mask. The position of the spot along the X-axis can be controlled by means of a reversible binary counter with an associated digital-to-analogue converter, while the output may be obtained in digital form by means of an analogue-to-digital converter fed with the Y-deflection voltage, suitably scaled.

Other methods of generating functions in analogue computer can be adapted by similar means to fit in a digital system, since these are of sufficient precision for a truly arbitrary function, although they are often inadequate, for generating other functions within the analogue computer which the d.d.a. can do with ease at full precision.

7.2.5 *Decision and switching*

The final functional type of operation necessary in a d.d.a. is that of making decisions based upon the value of a given variable and switching the course of the computation as a result. A simple example of this is stopping the solution of a problem when a certain parameter has reached a predetermined value. A more complex example is the solution of the equations representing a ball bouncing upon a hard surface; here, the change of direction of motion when the ball hits the surface can be introduced into the equations by deciding when the displacement of the ball is zero and switching the form of the equation when this happens, to take account of the change in sign of the velocity and the loss in momentum due to the coefficient of restitution.

In order to make a decision of this kind, a means must exist for setting the predetermined value of a parameter at which the decision occurs, and a means of forming the value of the variable from increments in it. These requirements correspond very closely with those for setting an initial value into an integrator and for updating the value of an integrand in the Y register with increments. If it is arranged for the predetermined value of the parameter to be set into the Y register at the beginning of a solution and for positive increments in y to decrease this value (and correspondingly, for negative increments in y to increase it), then the decision can be regarded as occurring when the sign of the contents of the Y register changes.

Further facilities can be provided which are similar to those convenient for use with an integrator. These include scaling the increments in y by a range of scaling factors, overflow detection if the value of y nears the maximum capacity of the Y register and resetting the initial value readily when a problem is repeated.

The switching function controlled by the decision is required to interrupt, close, or divert a path along which increments are flowing. All necessary control operations can be done in this way. The requirement can generally be met by means of an electronic version of a relay changeover contact, so that signals fed to the switch normally take one output path, but when the control signal from the decision function occurs, the signals are diverted to the alternative output path. This is very simple operation to provide and it is easy to arrange for a single control signal to control a number of switches. A useful facility in a switch is a visual indication of which path is open for the transmission of signals.

7.2.6 *Overall control*

In addition to the functional operations discussed in the preceding sections, facilities are required for the overall control of a d.d.a. of the simultaneous kind. Apart from the usual mains on and off switch, and so on, these can conveniently include:

independent variable on and off,
central display of contents of selected Y register,
stop control when the independent variable reaches a predetermined set
value,
a selection of independent variable rates to allow problems to be run at
different speeds.

7.3 Functional units

In the preceding section, the kind of facilities required in a simultaneous d.d.a. have been discussed, together with some other features which, whilst not essential, are useful and make a machine easier to operate. From the operational point of view the simultaneous d.d.a. comes very near to an analogue computer and it seems preferable to organize it from the user's point of view so that the facilities that he is accustomed to find on an analogue machine are made available also on this kind of d.d.a. He can then start using it with the very minimum of training.

There are two principle kinds of analogue computer operational layout. The first of these uses plug-in operational amplifiers and other units which can be placed into shelves in any desired layout and interconnected by means of patch-cords. This design has the advantage that the units can be laid out in a similar form to the disposition of the terms in the equations upon paper. It then becomes easy to find a unit associated with a given term, for example, when the value of the term is required to be known, or if a change in a coefficient value is necessary. A very close association between the computer set-up and the equations can be maintained with this kind of machine.

The other type of analogue machine uses a fixed layout of operational amplifiers and associated units, whose inputs and outputs are connected to fixed positions on a patchboard. This arrangement lacks the kind of flexibility of the previous type, but has flexibility of another kind, inasmuch as the machine can have the program changed very quickly by merely changing patchboards. This operation takes time on the first kind of machine, since a complete repatching of all units is necessary.

It can be seen that the first kind of machine is useful where a given problem is likely to remain for long periods of time and where a close association between the set-up and the problem is of assistance in simplifying the use of the equipment. The second kind is useful where a computing service is offered where users are likely to come along with totally different problems during the day and who are prepared to sacrifice the direct association of the equation layout with the equipment layout.

Either of these arrangements can be used for a simultaneous d.d.a., and the kind of use to which it is to be put will determine which is preferable for a given application. In either case, there is a great deal to be said for constructing the various operational units as entities and making these in the form of plug-in units, since this facilitates maintenance and replacement of faulty units. It can also allow a machine to be built up gradually from a few units to a larger number as the need arises. It is possible to conceive a machine which has the ability to take on the features of either of the arrangements mentioned. Such a machine would have inputs and outputs of each unit available on the unit for interconnexion by patch-cord but also would have them taken away through the main plug and socket in the racking to a central patchboard. Whilst this would be more costly than either of the other arrangements on their own, the machine would be extremely flexible.

It is possible to discuss the various units which can be used to construct a simultaneous d.d.a. incorporating the facilities already outlined. It will have been seen from the discussion that the basic integrator can be regarded as an integrator, coefficient multiplier or as part of a digital arbitrary function generator. The facilities required for all of these functions can be combined economically into one unit which is only slightly more complex than the integrator itself. The overall design of the computer will then be simplified with an associated saving in cost.

In the case of the adder, however, the extra complexity required to be built into an integrator to enable it to perform the addition function is too great to be justifiable and this function is better performed by a separate unit. Much the same arguments apply to the decision function and this is better performed as a separate function rather than as one of the facilities provided in an integrator.

In view of these considerations, the units required to construct a simultaneous d.d.a. can conveniently be as follows:

  (i) integrator/coefficient multiplier/part of arbitrary
        function generator;
  (ii) adder unit;
  (iii) decision unit;
  (iv) switch unit;
  (v)   arbitrary function generator.

In order to overcome drift problems in an integrator due to reversals in the signals representing the variable of integration, a corrected integrator can also be included, as required:

  (vi) Corrected integrator.

Apart from any control equipment required, these six units are adequate for constructing a simultaneous d.d.a. which is capable of solving differential equations with the facility equal to an analogue computer since it has all the same functions. The actual number of units required will, of course, depend upon the problems to be solved but it has been found that the six units specified allow a reasonably wide range of problems to be solved from a given number and distribution of unit types. This flexibility is due to the multipurpose nature of some of the units.

7.4 Input/output

Data which has to be supplied to the d.d.a. before it can commence the solution of a problem include:

(i) initial values of the integrands,
(ii) coefficient multiplier values,
(iii) any scaling values for increments,
(iv) values of variables at which decisions are required,
(v) arbitrary function characteristics.

The first four of these are quantities which can conveniently be set by means of multiposition switches associated with the appropriate units, as already discussed. The arbitrary function characteristics of the slope and turning points of the approximation to the function can be supplied either by means of paper or magnetic tape or, alternatively, on removable patchboards. The choice will depend, like the method of programming, upon the principal mode of use of the equipment.

Whilst there is some advantage in being able to set the initial values of integrands, coefficient multiplier values and values of variables at which decisions are required by an automatic means, such as punched paper or magnetic tape, it then becomes more difficult to make a change in any required value out of the set. One of the principal uses of a simultaneous d.d.a. is simulation, as already mentioned, and when the machine is being used in this way it is frequently necessary to try varying a parameter, such as a coefficient multiplier, to see what the effect is on the solution. To have to do this by preparing and inserting a tape each time would be clumsy and inconvenient. On balance, it seems preferable to set in these quantities by hand when the problem is first programmed and to have the facility for changing any one with ease. An intermediate solution is feasible in which a set of initial conditions is set up automatically by means of tape, but with facilities on each unit for this to be overruled locally. There is some danger of incorrect setting up with this approach since the units are not gone through systematically and it would be easy to overlook one altogether.

7.5 Applications

The techniques described above allow a simultaneous d.d.a. to be built which is capable of solving complex problems with minimum error. When used for axis transformation, as described in Chapter 6, section 7, the errors stated there which result from a machine without corrected integrators can be reduced by their use to a level where the d.d.a. solution is as accurate as that of a g.p. computer, the latter taking much longer over the computation.

8: Airborne Navigation

8.1 Introduction

Chapters 2, 3 and 4 have dealt with the basic properties of the d.d.a. integrator and how integrators can be connected to perform incremental calculations. Chapter 6 has also shown how a simulation exercise is carried out on a d.d.a.

Here we are concerned with an extension of the role of a d.d.a. into that of an airborne navigation computer used in conjunction with a general purpose (whole number) digital computer. In practice, the two can be considered as one machine with two sections and a common interface; a reference to such a machine, DEXAN, is made in the bibliography at the end of Chapter 1. It is assumed that the computer is mounted in and travels with the aircraft and is being fed continuously with input data from airborne sensors producing drift, heading, groundspeed and windspeed.

The complete task of airborne navigation is complex and some of the calculations have to be performed entirely by whole-number techniques. However, many calculations can be handled more efficiently by a d.d.a. and it is on these that emphasis has been placed.

Where calculations involve both the g.p. and d.d.a., reference has been made to appropriate parts of the g.p. program. To avoid the introduction of material not strictly relevant to the main purpose of the chapter, the g.p. programs not directly concerned with the d.d.a., such as those for navigational fixing techniques are mentioned only by name and not explained in detail.

Each of the primary data sensors is described in sufficient detail to show how the data is produced incrementally and thereafter used by a binary d.d.a. in which the zero rate is represented by alternate 1's and 0's where 1's represent a positive step and 0's a negative step.

8.2 The Doppler radar

The Doppler radar set used for aircraft navigation provides outputs representing distance gone and drift angle, shown in Figure 8.1. 'Doppler distance gone' arises from a shaft in the set which rotates at an angular speed proportional to the speed of the aircraft along its 'track'. The movement of this shaft is transmitted electrically to another which drives a 'digital tachometer' (described in 8.4) producing an incremental input suitable for the d.d.a. Each increment corresponds to a fixed distance moved by the aircraft along its track.

Drift angle, the angle between the direction the aircraft is heading and that of its track over the earth's surface, also arises from a shaft in the radar. The position of this shaft is transmitted electrically to another in the computer which drives a digital tachometer and a digitizer. The tachometer provides increments of drift angle as an input to the d.d.a. and the digitizer provides a 'whole number' (as opposed to incremental) input of drift angle to the g.p.

The convention used is that drift angle ψ_D is positive when the track of the aircraft lies to starboard (the right) of the heading. Figure 8.1 shows a case where ψ_D is positive.

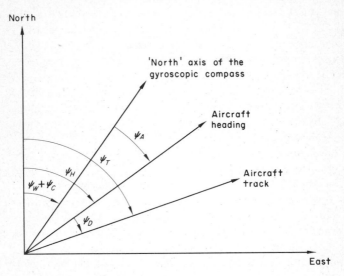

Figure 8.1. *Definition of angles*

ψ_A *'azimuth angle' from the gyroscopic compass.*
ψ_D *'drift angle' from the Doppler radar.*
ψ_C *'azimuth correction angle' computed by whole number.*
ψ_H *the aircraft's heading angle.*
ψ_T *the aircraft's track angle.*
ψ_W *'wander angle' of the gyroscopic compass.*

8.3 The heading reference

For navigation to be carried out with Doppler radar, the computer must be able to calculate the direction of the aircraft's track with respect to North. This is the track angle shown as ψ_T in Figure 8.1 and it has two components, the drift angle ψ_D obtained from the Doppler radar and the heading angle ψ_H from a 'heading reference'. Two types of heading reference commonly used are the magnetic and gyroscopic compasses.

A magnetic compass provides the heading angle of the aircraft with respect to magnetic North. To this must be added the 'magnetic deviation' which is the angle between 'true' and magnetic North. This correction from magnetic to true heading is generally carried out by the navigator who adjusts a magnetic deviation control to the value appropriate to the current aircraft position.

When flights are carried out in the vicinity of the magnetic poles, i.e. at 'high' latitudes, magnetic compasses become unusable and it is here that gyroscopic compasses are valuable.

The gyroscopic compass, or more briefly the gyro-compass, relies on the fact that a gyroscope always attempts to keep its axis pointing in a fixed direction in space. It consists, basically, of a single gyroscope the axis of which is restrained to lie in the horizontal plane.

The heading angle obtained from a gyro-compass, however, also requires correction since it develops an angular error at a rate which is equal to the local vertical component of the aircraft's rate of rotation about the earth's North-South axis. This rate of rotation is made up of two terms, one is the earth's rate of rotation and the other is the rate of change of the aircraft's longitude. The total angular error due to this cause is called the 'wander angle' ψ_W, given by the equation:

$$\psi_W = \int \Omega \sin \lambda \, dt + \int \sin \lambda \, d\mu \qquad (1)$$

where Ω is the earth's rate of rotation. It is assumed that the integration is carried out from the time and position where the heading angle was correct.

The term 'gyro-magnetic' is applied to a type of compass which for the purposes of this chapter is regarded as a magnetic compass since it indicates magnetic heading and requires a magnetic deviation correction. The advantage of this type is that it combines the self-setting capability of the magnetic compass with that of the gyro-compass to indicate the correct heading despite violent aircraft manoeuvres. It consists of a gyroscope which is con-

trolled by a magnetic sensing device so that it points to the magnetic North.
The heading angle from the compass system, whether it is magnetic or gyroscopic, can be transmitted to the computer by one of two methods. The first is the same as that used for the drift angle from the Doppler radar where an electrical transmission causes a shaft to follow the heading angle. The shaft is geared to a digital tachometer, which feeds increments of heading to the d.d.a., and to a digitizer which provides a 'whole number' input to the g.p.

The second method assumes the compass system is already fitted with a digitizer which provides the whole number input required for the g.p. It is shown in Section 8.5 how the d.d.a. can be used to produce an incremental input from this whole number source if desired.

The digitizers, which give the whole number inputs of heading, are arranged to pass through their complete set of values each time the heading changes by 2π radians. This number can be scaled by program to represent radians divided by π. Since it has been assumed that a number n must lie within the range:

$$-1 \leqslant n \leqslant +1 - 2^{-19}$$

it would appear that an anomalous result is possible when, for example, the addition of 2^{-19} to $+1 - 2^{-19}$ produces -1, or when the reverse happens as 2^{-19} is subtracted from -1. This point is dealt with in the context of programming in Chapter 3.

However, when the number represents an angle in radians divided by π then the above example corresponds to the addition of $2^{-19}\pi$ radians to $(+1 - 2^{-19})\pi$ radians producing the result π radians. For most navigation purposes this is a convenient result since angles lying outside the range $-\pi$ to $+\pi$ are generally not of interest.

8.4 The digital tachometer

As mentioned previously, the digital tachometer is coupled either mechanically or electrically to a shaft and, by means of associated circuitry, produces an incremental signal which may be used as a Δx or a Δy input to a d.d.a. integrator.

Since a binary d.d.a. is being considered, the incremental signal produced when the tachometer is not turning consists of alternate 0's and 1's. When the tachometer rotates through an angle corresponding to one increment in the positive direction an extra 1 is inserted into this sequence and rotation of the same amount in the negative direction causes an extra 0 to be inserted. The maximum allowable rate of rotation corresponds to a sequence of all 1's or all 0's.

To avoid exceeding the maximum rate of rotation the gearing, through which the tachometer is coupled to its shaft, must be arranged so that when the shaft is turning at its maximum speed the rate at which increments are produced does not exceed the iteration rate of the d.d.a. Assume, for example, an iteration rate of 234 cycles/second and that the shaft turns at a maximum rate of 10 degrees/second, then, since not more than 134 increments must be produced each second, the increment must not be less than $\frac{10}{234}$ degrees. Conveniently, an increment value of 0·05 degree can be used.

8.5 Production of an incremental input from a 'whole number' source

By means of a special facility in DEXAN an incremental rate can be produced for an input which is only available as a whole number value from a digitizer. The facility allows an integrator to be programmed so that its ΔZ output corresponds to the sign of the difference between the number obtained from the digitizer and the number Y in the Y register. (The reader must note here that we are dealing with a sequential, binary d.d.a.)

The ΔZ output is fed back as a ΔY input and is thus able to change Y. If $D - Y$ is positive or zero, ΔZ is a one and Y is caused to increase by one increment. If $D - Y$ is negative ΔZ is a zero and Y decreases. If D is stationary a position will be reached where Y is alternately one increment greater than and then equal to D.

8.6 The d.d.a. program

[Before dealing with this section it must be explained that the method of integrator representation and indication of scaling used differ from those described in Chapter 3.

The negative power of two applied to the ΔY inputs before accumulation is indicated by a small number (called the ΔY scale number in the text) written near the output end of the integrator. This ΔY scale number corresponds to the register length N mentioned in Chapter 3. Y numbers are shown in the normal position but the bottom line of the integrator is used to separate numerator from denominator. The flow lines similarly separate numerator and denominator for the ΔX and ΔY inputs and ΔZ outputs.

The scaling factor applied to an incremental problem variable (see Figures 8.8 and 8.9) can conveniently be regarded as 'incremental pulses per unit'. To understand this, consider the incremental output of integrator 96 of Figure 8.9. The factor is $1/2^3$ or an eighth, meaning that an eighth of a pulse is equivalent to each unit of S moved. In practice this means one pulse at the output of integrator 96 is produced for each 8 feet increase in S.

For an example of the ΔY scale number see integrator 13 in Figure 8.8. The input is $2^{19}\Delta\lambda/\pi$ and the ΔY scale number is 19. Hence the Y number of 13 is $2^{-19}\Sigma 2^{19}$ $\Delta\lambda/\pi = \lambda/\pi$. It is shown in Chapter 2 that the relationship $\Delta Z = Y \Delta X$ applies directly.

It should be noted that Figures 8.2 to 8.6 are intended to demonstrate the principles used in the application of a d.d.a. to airborne navigation and that no scaling details are given. Figures 8.8 and 8.9 however, which give the complete d.d.a. schematic described in Section 8.13 carry full details of the scaling.]

The tachometers, T1, T2 and T3 to the left of Figure 8.2 provide incremental inputs of drift angle, heading angle and Doppler distance gone respectively to integrators 32, 64 and 96.

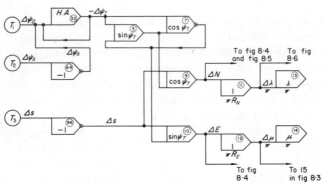

Figure 8.2. Part of the d.d.a. program.

The first function carried out is the resolution of increments of Doppler distance gone (ΔS) into incremental distances moved north (ΔN) and east (ΔE). This is done by mechanizing the equations:

$$\left.\begin{array}{l}\Delta N = \Delta S \cos \psi_T \\ \Delta E = \Delta S \sin \psi_T\end{array}\right\} \qquad (2)$$

where the track angle ψ_T is given by:

$$\psi_T = \psi_A + \psi_D . \qquad (3)$$

(It will be assumed for the moment that the angle ψ_A from the heading reference is accurate and requires no correction.)

In the case being considered each tachometer provides an incremental input which can only be used by a set of associated integrators. Integrator 96, one of a set able to receive an input from T3, serves only to make ΔS available as an input to integrators 9 and 10. It does not rescale ΔS. The Y numbers of integrators 9 and 10 are cos ψ_T and sin ψ_T and their outputs are the required ΔN and ΔE.

In order to keep these Y numbers correct it is necessary to form $\Delta\psi_T = \Delta\psi_A + \Delta\psi_D$. This is done by the 'hard adder', integrator 32, which in fact, due to the sign change which occurs through it, actually produces $-\Delta\psi_T$. The inputs to the hard adder are $\Delta\psi_D$ which comes directly from T_1 and $\Delta\psi_A$ which is made available by integrator 64.

Integrators 5 and 7 form a sine-cosine loop. The sign change of the ΔZ output is associated with the integrator holding the cosine term, however, and not with that holding the sine term as has been shown in previous chapters. This has the effect of compensating for the negative sign of the output of the hard adder 32. The outputs of integrators 5 and 7 are used not only to keep their own Y numbers correct but also the necessary ΔY inputs for integrators 9 and 10.

The next step, once ΔN and ΔE have been produced is to convert these into increments of latitude $\Delta\lambda$ and longitude $\Delta\mu$ according to the equations:

$$\left. \begin{array}{l} \Delta\lambda = \Delta N/R_N \\ \Delta\mu = \Delta E/R_E \end{array} \right\} \tag{4}$$

by integrators 11 and 12 respectively. R_N is the North-South radius of curvature of the earth's surface, and R_E the distance from the aircraft to the earth's spin axis. The Y numbers of integrators 11 and 12 are called the 'earth terms' and are computed by the g.p. computer.

The factor $1/\pi$ associated with these terms is necessary in order to produce increments of $\Delta\lambda/\pi$ and $\Delta\mu/\pi$, accumulated by integrators 13 and 14, to give latitude and longitude scaled as 'radians divided by π'.

8.7 Computation of 'wander angle'

The 'wander angle' for a gyroscopic compass given by equation (1) is rearranged as:

$$\frac{\Delta\psi_W}{\pi} = \frac{\Omega \sin \lambda \Delta t}{\pi} + \frac{\sin \lambda \Delta\mu}{\pi}. \tag{5}$$

Figure 8.3 shows how this is computed in the d.d.a.

The output of integrator 12 (Figure 8.2) is multiplied by $\lambda \sin \lambda$ in integrator 15 to produce the extreme right-hand term of equation (5). The other right-hand term is produced by integrator 16 which has a ΔX input of full machine

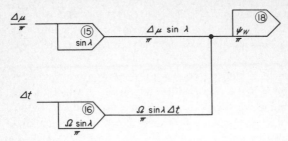

Figure 8.3. Part of the d.d.a. program.

rate, denoted by Δt. The outputs of integrators 15 and 16 are then accumulated in integrator 18 to give a suitably scaled 'wander angle'.

The g.p. program periodically resets the Y numbers of integrators 15 and 16. The frequency at which these terms are corrected is such that no significant error occurs in the computed wander angle.

8.8 Computation of wind velocity

The northerly and easterly components of wind velocity can be computed from a knowledge of the aircraft's airspeed. The distance the aircraft moves North in time Δt is the distance it moves through the air in the northerly direction plus the distance the air moves in the same direction in the same time. This distance must be equal to the distance moved North according to the Doppler radar. Hence:

$$V_A \Delta t \cos \psi_H + V_N \Delta t = \Delta N \tag{6}$$

where V_A is the airspeed, ψ_H the heading angle and V_N the northerly component of wind velocity. Similarly by considering the movements in the easterly direction:

$$V_A \Delta t \sin \psi_H + V_E \Delta t = \Delta E \tag{7}$$

where V_E is the easterly component of the wind velocity.

Equations (6) and (7) are used to produce the terms $V_N \Delta t$ and $V_E \Delta t$. From these 'smoothed' values of the components of wind velocity, W_N and W_E are produced by equations which take the form:

$$\left. \begin{array}{c} W_N + T \dfrac{d}{dt}(W_N) = V_N \\[2mm] W_E + T \dfrac{d}{dt}(W_E) = V_E . \end{array} \right\} \tag{9}$$

These equations are re-arranged for d.d.a. computation as:

$$T \Delta W_{\mathrm{N}} = V_{\mathrm{N}} \Delta t - W_{\mathrm{N}} \Delta t$$

and
$$T \Delta W_{\mathrm{E}} = V_{\mathrm{E}} \Delta t - W_{\mathrm{E}} \Delta t . \tag{10}$$

The time constant T can be of the order of 30 to 60 seconds.

By subsituting from equations (6) and (7) in equations (10) we get:

$$T \Delta W_{\mathrm{N}} = \Delta \mathrm{N} - V_{\mathrm{A}} \Delta t \cos \psi_{\mathrm{H}} - W_{\mathrm{N}} \Delta t$$
$$T \Delta W_{\mathrm{E}} = \Delta \mathrm{E} - V_{\mathrm{A}} \Delta t \sin \psi_{\mathrm{H}} - W_{\mathrm{E}} \Delta t . \tag{11}$$

These equations are mechanized by the arrangement shown in Figure 8.4.

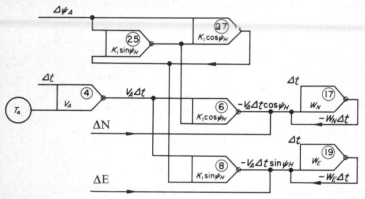

Figure 8.4. Part of the d.d.a. program.

$\Delta \mathrm{N}$ and $\Delta \mathrm{E}$ are available already as the output of integrators 9 and 10. Integrators 25 and 27 are necessary to produce the sine and cosine of the heading angle and to keep the Y numbers of integrators 6 and 8 correct. It should be noted that the input to the sine cosine loop is $\Delta \psi_A$ ($\Delta \psi_A$ is the uncorrected output of the heading reference) whereas the integrators are shown as holding the sine and cosine of ψ_{H}. The correction is introduced by the g.p. program which periodically resets the contents of integrators 6, 8, 25 and 27.

The airspeed is set into integrator 4 by the g.p. and kept correct by an incremental input from the digital tachometer T4.

8.9 A 'reversionary mode' of navigation

The reason for computing the components of wind velocity is that if the Doppler radar fails then navigation can continue in a reversionary mode from the air speed and the last computed values of the wind velocity components.

The change to the reversionary mode is carried out automatically by the d.d.a. On receipt of a 'failure' signal from the Doppler radar one ΔY input on each of two integrators is inhibited and another input received in its place. This switching of ΔY inputs is arranged to alter the d.d.a. program so that instead of navigating from ΔN and ΔE derived from the Doppler it navigates from similar quantities derived from the air speed and the last computed values of the wind velocity components, as given by equations (6) and (7) with V_N and V_E replaced by W_N and W_E respectively. The switching, when it occurs, is arranged in such a way that these values remain stationary whilst the reversionary mode is in operation. If the failure is not permanent the

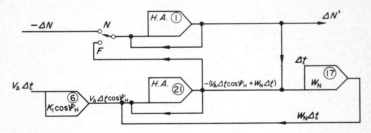

Figure 8.5. Part of the d.d.a. program.

failure signal from the Doppler radar will disappear and the program then reverts back to its former mode of operation.

Figure 8.5 shows how the switching is arranged for the North-South part of the program.

The hard adder 21 is used to produce as its output:

$$- (V_A \Delta t \cos \psi_H + W_N \Delta t)$$

and this is part of the ΔY input to integrator 17. The remainder of the ΔY input required by this integrator is supplied by the hard adder 1.

Integrator 1 is one of the two integrators whose ΔY inputs are switched by the failure signal and this is shown in the figure as a switch which connects the required input. Normally this lies in position N when $-\Delta N$, obtained by changing the sign of integrator 9 in Figure 8.2, is received. The output of 1 in this case is ΔN and is used for navigation purposes and also to enable the smoothed northerly wind component W_N to be computed.

When the failure signal is received the switch changes to position F and the output of the hard adder 21 is now used as an input to integrator 1. This has the result firstly of causing the sum of the ΔY inputs to integrator 17 to be zero since they consist of the output of the hard adder 21 and the negative of the same quantity as its sign is changed on passing through the hard adder 1. This causes W_N to remain at its last computed value. Secondly, the output of integrator 1 which is used for navigation becomes:

$$V_A \Delta t \cos \psi_H + W_N \Delta t$$

so that the required reversion has been achieved.

The output of integrator 1 has been called $\Delta N'$ to distinguish it from ΔN which it equals only in the normal mode of navigation. Similarly the East-West part of the program produces the quantity $\Delta E'$.

8.10 The position and wind displays

Integrators can be used to produce outputs suitable for driving special motors called 'M' motors. In these the shaft takes up one of six positions depending upon the polarities of the voltages applied to its three input leads. If the polarities change in a suitable manner the M motor shaft can be made to rotate step by step in a required direction. Circuitry associated with each of the integrators is arranged to produce the three voltages required by the M motors. When the integrator produces a ΔZ rate which is positive the voltages change in a cyclic fashion and cause the motor to rotate in its 'positive' direction. If the ΔZ rate is negative the voltages change through the reverse of their positive sequence and the motor rotates in its negative direction.

Since a binary d.d.a. is used, it is necessary to prevent zero rate producing a vibratory movement of the M motors. This is done by only allowing the voltages to change when two successive ΔZ's from the integrator are identical, i.e. two 1's or two 0's; thus zero rate causes no change in the voltages.

M motors can be used to drive displays of latitude and longitude in degrees and minutes and the wind velocities in knots. Figure 8.6 shows the arrangements needed to drive these displays. The four integrators on the right of the figure are associated with the displays concerned. The latitude and longitude 'channels' in this figure are identical as are the wind 'channels' so that only one of each will be described.

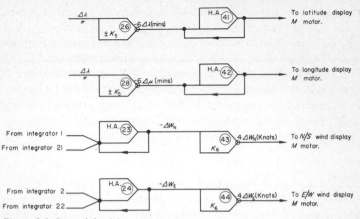

Figure 8.6. *Part of the d.d.a. program.*

The latitude channel uses as its input the output of integrator 11 of Figure 8.2. This is scaled by a constant K_5 in integrator 26 which is needed to produce steps of the correct size (corresponding to one-sixth of a minute of arc in this case). Integrator 26 produces a negative ΔZ to compensate for the hard adder which follows and which is used to produce the drive for the latitude display M motor.

Two functions of the g.p. program are associated with the latitude channel. The first is necessary since the display only shows the modulus of the latitude. Sign reversal of the drive, which is required on crossing the equator, is carried out by a part of the g.p. program which sets the sign of the constant K_5 in integrator 26 to be the same as that of the latitude in integrator 13. The sign of the latitude is automatically displayed on a device known as a 'flag indicator' as an 'N' or an 'S'. The flag indicator is controlled directly by the sign digit of integrator 13.

The second function of the g.p. program with respect to this channel is concerned with ensuring that the reading shown by the display corresponds to the latitude held in integrator 13. Each display is geared to a digitizer which enables the g.p. computer to determine what reading is being shown. To keep the displayed latitude correct the g.p. program periodically reads the associated digitizer, forms the error between the computed latitude from integrator 13 and that given by the digitizer reading, converts this into the number of M motor steps needed to correct the display which it then adds into the Y number of the hard adder, integrator 41. The hard adder then produces the correct number of extra ΔZ pulses and causes the display to take up the correct reading.

The North-South wind display channel obtains its input by combining the outputs of the hard adders 1 and 21 in the hard adder 23 to produce $-\Delta W_N$. This is scaled by K_6 in integrator 43 to the correct step size to drive the wind display and also has its sign corrected. The g.p. program is again used to ensure that the correct value of wind component is displayed. In this case, however, it computes the number of ΔW_N steps required and places the correct function of this number in the hard adder 23.

Before describing the remainder of the d.d.a. program it is convenient to describe the part played by the g.p. in more detail.

8.11 The part played by the g.p. computer
The work done by the g.p. computer consists of:

(i)   reading in and checking that both the g.p. and d.d.a. programs have been correctly inserted into the store, then starting the d.d.a.

(ii)   reading in whole number values from digitizers

(iii)   resetting sin/cosine loops

(iv)   computing slowly changing terms

(v)   correcting the displays

(vi)   reading in fix positions

(vii)   carrying out fixing operations

(viii)   calculation of correction factors.

The first role of the g.p. is to read into the store both its own and the d.d.a. programs. It is assumed that the programs are not retained when the computer is switched off and that programs are read in by means of a photoelectric tape reader. When reading has been completed the g.p. program is automatically started and carries out a 'sum check' which involves summing the contents of all location in the store and checking the result against the known sum. By choosing the contents of one of the locations correctly this known sum can be made zero. If the sum is found to be incorrect the program stops the g.p. and this indicates to the operator that the sum check has failed. If the sum is correct the g.p. starts the d.d.a. which so far has been stopped, then continues with the remainder of its own program.

The path taken by this program now consists of a loop through which it cycles periodically. The only departures from this loop occur when the sign digit of an associated integrator in the d.d.a. is changed from negative to positive. This signifies to the g.p. that a departure from its normal loop is required. It then leaves the loop, carries out the operation specified, sets the sign of the integrator back to negative and returns to the loop. The sign digits are changed by the operation of control buttons or switches located on a control panel.

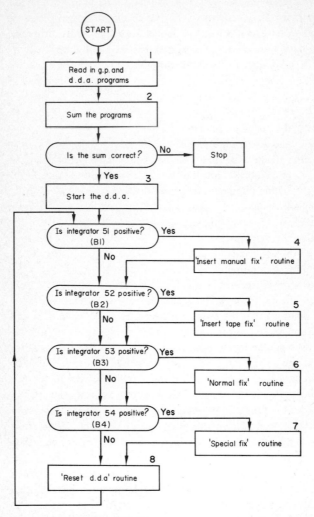

Figure 8.7. G.P. flow diagram.

8.12 The g.p. program

A flow diagram of the g.p. program is given in Figure 8.7. Blocks 1 to 3 of this diagram are straightforward and need no description. The next four routines carry out their functions and alter the contents of integrator 60, shown in Figure 8.8, which controls a lamp display of computer functions associated with position fixing operations. These lights indicate the state of the g.p. program so far as the fixing sequence is concerned. For example, if no data has been initially inserted or the sequence has just been completed (by routines 6 and 7) then the lights are set to zero to indicate that the computer is not ready to perform a fix calculation. When the operator inserts the co-ordinates of a fix point (using buttons B1 or B2, as shown in Figure 8.8) the state of the lights then indicate that a fix may be carried out.

The details of blocks 4 to 8 are as follows:

Block 4. *Manual data insertion routine*

Read the latitude and longitude, 'set' display digitizers.

Scale the readings to radians divided by π and store for use during fixing.

Set integrator 60 to display the number 15 on the lights.

Reset integrator 51 negative.

Block 5. *Tape data insertion routine*

Read the fix point position and number from punched paper tape.

Store the position for use during fixing.

Store the fix number in integrator 60 to show it on the lights.

Reset integrator 52 negative.

Block 6. *Normal fixing routine*

Set the present fix point position co-ordinates into integrators 13 and 14 and also store them as 'last fix point co-ordinates'.

Set zero into integrator 60.

Reset integrator 53 negative.

Block 7. *'Fix Monitored Azimuth'* (f.m.a.) *fixing routine*

Store the computed position co-ordinates from integrators 13 and 14 and reset these integrators with the present fix point co-ordinates.

From the co-ordinates of the computed position, present fix point position and last fix point position compute the error in ψ_C, the azimuth correction angle.

Correct ψ_C.

Store the present fix point co-ordinates as the 'last fix point co-ordinates'.

Set zero into integrator 60.

Reset integrator 54 negative.

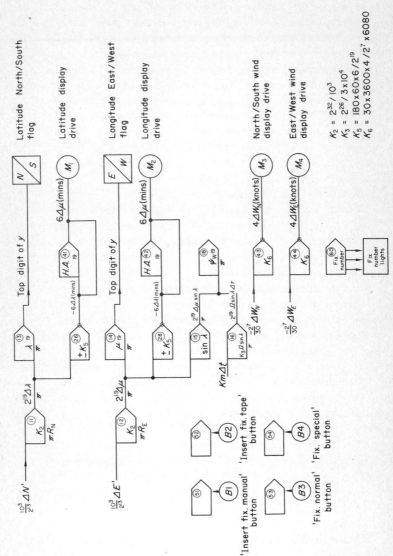

Figure 8.8. Computation of latitude, longitude and wander angle.

Block 8. *The 'reset d.d.a.' routine*

Set the airspeed into integrator 4.

Reset the track sin/cosine terms in integrators 5, 7, 9 and 10.

Reset the heading sin/cosine terms in integrators 25, 27, 6 and 8.

Compute the earth terms and reset integrators 11 and 12.

Reset integrators 15 and 16.

Set the sign of K_5 in integrators 26 and 28 the same as the signs of integrators 13 and 14 respectively.

Correct the latitude display.

Correct the longitude display.

Correct the N/S wind display.

Correct the E/W wind display.

8.13 The complete d.d.a. schematic

The complete d.d.a. schematic of the navigation program is given in Figures 8.8 and 8.9. Figure 8.8 shows the part of the d.d.a. program which deals with computation of latitude (λ), longitude (μ) and wander angle (ψ_w), with the display of λ, μ and the components of wind velocity, with the four control buttons (B_1 to B_4) and with the fix number light display.

Figure 8.9 shows the part of the program which deals with the resolution of Doppler distance gone into incremental distances moved North and East (ΔN and ΔE), the computation of components of wind velocity and with reversion to navigation from airspeed and last computed components of wind velocity in the case of Doppler failure.

Where an integrator has no ΔY inputs, no ΔY scale number has been given since the scale number does not affect the operation of these integrators. In practice, since some scale number must be used, it is most convenient to use 19.

On these two figures units of feet, seconds and radians are used except where other units are indicated. The constants which are given have been left in a form which shows the factors from which they are made up and allows an easy check on the scaling to be made. The factor K_m, by which Δt is shown scaled at the ΔX input of certain integrators, is the iteration rate of the d.d.a. Also the same integrator numbering has been used as in the earlier figures. This section of the chapter will be devoted to explaining the difference between the complete schematic and the earlier diagrams, how the wind computations are scaled and how the various scaling constants are derived.

In Figure 8.8 there are five integrators not previously shown. Four of these,

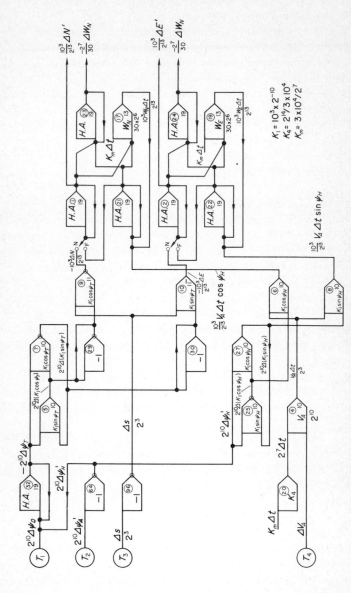

Figure 8.9. Resolution of Doppler, computation of wind velocities and reversion.

51 to 54, are connected with the control buttons B1 to B4 mentioned in Section 8.12. When one of these is pressed, it causes the sign digit of the associated integrator to change so that its contents become positive. The fifth integrator is 60 which holds the number to be shown on the 'fix number' lights. This number may be between 1 and 15.

Two new integrators shown in Figure 8.9 are 29 and 30. These are necessary to prevent the drift error, described in Chapter 4, occurring in integrators 9 and 10. If uncorrected, this drift results in a gradual change in the displayed latitude and longitude with the aircraft stationary. It is overcome by preventing the integrator Y number from changing when zero rate occurs, by feeding the ΔY input to the integrator both directly and via a 'delay' integrator. This causes the increments fed through it to arrive one cycle later. Thus when zero rate occurs it produces a delayed zero rate having 1's and 0's where the original rate had 0's and 1's respectively. When these two rates are used as ΔY inputs to an integrator no change occurs to the Y number.

In a sequential d.d.a. an integrator, not processed between the two being connected, can be used as a delay, thus integrator 29 can be used to delay the output of 5 before feeding it to 9, since 29 does not lie between 5 and 9. Similarly integrator 30 serves as a delay between 7 and 10.

The total ΔY input to integrator 9 amounts to twice the output of integrator 5, i.e. it is $2^{11} \Delta (K_1 \cos \psi_T)$ and for this reason 9 is given a ΔY scale of 11. Similarly integrator 10 also has a ΔY scale of 11.

It is not considered necessary to apply this technique of drift error elimination to integrators 6 and 8 since it would cause no significant improvement in the lower accuracy reversionary mode of navigation.

The K_1 term by which the track and heading sin/cosine terms in this figure is scaled is $10^3 \times 2^{-10}$. This constant, just less than unity, is necessary to prevent these terms overflowing when drift occurs.

Integrator 20 is necessary to provide $2^7 \Delta t$ as the input to integrator 4 to ensure that the outputs of integrator 6 and 8 have the same scaling, on input to the part of the schematic that deals with the wind computations, as those of integrators 9 and 10, namely feet $\times 10^3 \times 2^{-13}$.

In order to determine the scaling constant applied to W_N it is assumed initially that integrator 17 holds $K_S W_N$. Its output will then be:

$$3 \times 10^4 \times 2^{-7} K_S W_N \Delta t .$$

For this to have the same scaling as the other inputs to integrator 21 we require that:

$$3 \times 10^4 \times 2^{-7} K_S = 10^3 \times 2^{-13}$$

i.e. $K_S = \frac{1}{30} \times 2^6$ and this is the value shown in Figure 8.9.

We now need to determine the ΔY scale number for integrator 17. Assume initially that the scale number is p. By considering the inputs to integrator 17 when the normal mode of navigation is in use (i.e. the 'switch' at the input of integrator 1 is at N) we get:

$$\Delta \frac{W_N}{30 \times 2} = 2^{-p} \frac{10^3}{2^{13}} \Delta N - \frac{10^3}{2^{13}} V_A \Delta t \cos \psi_A - \frac{10^3}{2^{13}} W_N \Delta t \, .$$

Using equation (6) this can be reduced to:

$$2^p \cdot \frac{2^{13}}{10^3} \cdot \frac{1}{30 \times 2^6} \Delta W_N = V_N \Delta t - W_N \Delta t$$

which has the same form as equation (10) and shows that the time constant of this equation is given by:

$$T = \frac{2^{p-7}}{3 \times 10^4} \text{ seconds} \, .$$

For this to be between 30 and 60 seconds we take $p = 13$ which gives a value of approximately 35 seconds.

Now that p has been determined we see that the total ΔY input to integrator 17 must be $2^7/30 \, \Delta W_N$ and thus the output of the hard adder, integrator 23, is the negative of this, as is shown in Figure 8.9.

K_2 is determined by applying $\Delta Z = Y \Delta X$ to integrator 11 which gives:

$$\frac{2^{19}}{\pi} \Delta \lambda = \frac{10^3}{2^{13}} \Delta N' \frac{K_2}{R_N} \, .$$

Since $\Delta \lambda = \Delta N'/R_N$ we get:

$$K_2 = 2^{32}/10^3 \pi \, .$$

At first sight this constant may appear rather large since it exceeds 10^6, but the value of R_N by which it is divided is of the order of 20×10^6 feet so that the result is well below unity.

By a similar calculation the value of K_3 is determined and it is given on the figure. This too appears large but is offset by Ω in this case which, being the earth's rate of rotation in radians per second, is very small.

The constant K_5 is necessary to convert the outputs of integrators 11 and

12 to minutes (of arc) × 6 since the M motors M_1 and M_2 require six steps to move the display by one minute. Using the relationship:

$$\frac{(\text{radians})}{\pi} = \frac{(\text{minutes})}{180 \times 60}$$

and applying the same method as before, we obtain the value of K_5; K_6 converts ΔW_N and ΔW_i to 'knots × 4' since the wind display M motors require 4 steps to change the display by one knot. It can be calculated using the relationship:

$$(\text{knots}) = \frac{(\text{nautical miles})}{(\text{hours})} = \frac{6080\ (\text{feet})}{3600\ (\text{seconds})}.$$

The Simulation of an Electrical Fault Applied to a High-Voltage Grid System

A.1 Definition of the problem

The equations to be solved represent the behaviour of an electrical machine shown in Figure A.1, relative to a similar machine of reference which is at a constant voltage e_r. The machine consists of a steam turbine-driven alternator delivering its rated power to a high voltage grid system via a step-up transformer. The grid system is assumed to keep at a constant voltage e and the alternator is in synchronism with it

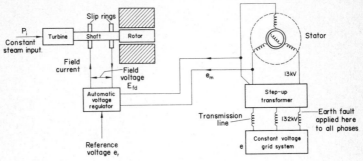

Figure A.1. *The system being simulated.*

A symmetrical fault is applied to all the high-voltage terminals of the transformer for a specified interval. This removes the load from the machine so that the steam power, which is assumed to remain constant, causes it to run away out of synchronism with the reference machine. The time the effect of such a fault takes to clear depends on the system parameters such as the length of time the fault is applied, the inertia of the rotor, etc. It is a difficult task to investigate the effect of changes in all the parameters. However, by using the machine in the manner to be described, this task proved to be relatively easy.

The parameters of interest (see Table A.1) during and after the fault, are the machine voltage and power, the exciter voltage and current and the extent the machine is out of phase with the reference machine. Values of

Table A.1

Variable	Initial value	End of fault	Step function (if any)	Final value
$e_m - e_r$	-0.701	-0.722	-0.262	0
$E_{fdo} - E$	-3.66	-3.29	-4.51	-0.371
e_m	0.402	0.381	0.842	1.103
e_{dm}	0	0	0.820	0.469
$E_{fdo} - E_{fd}/T_{do}$	0	-0.547	-0.547	0
i_q	0	0	0.482	0.275
e_{qm}	0.402	0.381	0.191	0.91
$P_i - P_u$	0.8	0.8	-2.22	0
$d\Delta/dt$	0	6.25	6.25	0
$e \sin \Delta$	0.589	0.789	0.789	0.437
$e \cos \Delta$	0.809	-0.378	-0.378	0.758
Δ	0.63	2.0	2.0	0.524
$-E_Q$	-5.56	-5.242	-6.25	-2.87

initial conditions associated with these parameters were set up to an accuracy of 1 in 2^{14} using a decimal binary converter for each appropriate integrator in turn.

A.2 The basic equations

The equation of motion of the rotor is

$$\frac{H}{180f} \frac{d^2 \delta}{dt^2} + K_D \frac{d\delta}{dt} + P_u = P_i$$

or

$$\frac{d^2 \Delta}{dt^2} + D \frac{d\Delta}{dt} = \frac{\omega}{2H} (P_i - P_u) \tag{1}$$

where the rotor angle is δ (degrees), Δ (radians) measured with respect to a fixed frame of reference, $\omega/2H$ is the inertia constant of the rotor, having dimension (seconds)$^{-2}$, P_i is the prime mover input power, which is assumed constant, D is damping (seconds)$^{-1}$ varying between runs and P_u is given by

$$P_u = E_Q i_q \tag{2}$$

where

$$E_Q = e_{qm} + x_{qm} i_d \tag{3}$$

$$i_q = e_{dm}/x_{qm} \tag{3}$$

x_{qm} is a constant being the quadrature axis synchronous reactance, e_{dm} and e_{qm} are the direct axis and quadrature axis components of e_m or

$$e_m = (e_{dm}^2 + e_{qm}^2)^{\frac{1}{2}} \tag{5}$$

where
$$e_{dm} = K_q e \sin \delta \tag{6}$$

K_q being a constant, and

$$e_{qm} = E - x_{dm} i_d \tag{7}$$

where x_{dm} is a constant being the direct axis synchronous reactance and i_d is given by

$$e \cos \delta = E - \frac{1}{K_d} x_{dm} i_d \tag{8}$$

E being the field excitation, a variable, measured in terms of the terminal voltage, produced on an open circuit with normal speed operation, and K_d a constant.

Now
$$T_{d_0} \frac{d\psi_{fd}}{dt} = E_{fd} - E$$

where E_{fd} is the excitation voltage referred to the armature and ψ_{fd} is given by

$$\psi_{fd} = E - (x_{dm} - x'_{dm}) i_d .$$

Then
$$\frac{E - E_{fd}}{T_{d_0}} = \frac{d}{dt} [E - (x_{dm} - x'_{dm}) i_d] , \tag{9}$$

T_{d_0} being the field time constant and x'_{dm} the transient reactance. Now E_{fd} is given by

$$E_{fd} = E_{fd_0} + \frac{\mu(e_r - e_m)}{1 + T_e (dE_{fd}/dt)} .$$

Then
$$[E_{fd} - E_{fd_0}][1 + T_e (dE_{fd}/dt)] = \mu(e_r - e_m)$$

i.e.
$$T_e (dE_{fd}/dt) + (E_{fd} - E_{fd_0}) = \mu(e_r - e_m) , \tag{10}$$

e_r being the terminal voltage of the reference machine, T_e the exciter time constant and μ the constant of proportionality of the voltage regulator.

A.3 The program

Because the complete flow diagram occupies a disproportionate amount of space it is not included in this appendix. Instead specimen interconnexions

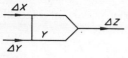

$$\Delta Z = Y\Delta X/N$$

Figure A.2(a). General integrator schematic.

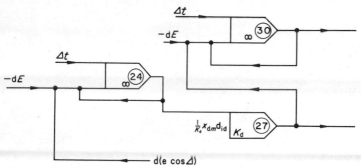

Figure A.2(b). Schematic for equation 8.

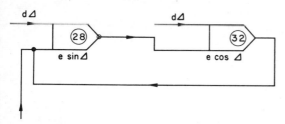

Figure A.2(c). Schematic for the sine-cosine loop.

are shown in Figures A.2(a), (b) and (c) which will enable the reader to see the general relationships.

The equations (1)–(10) are to be solved in incremental form as follows:
(1) becomes

$$\frac{d}{dt}\left(\frac{d\Delta}{dt}\right) + D\frac{d\Delta}{dt} = \frac{\omega}{2H}(P_i - P_u)$$

i.e.

$$d\left(\frac{d\Delta}{dt}\right) = -Dd\Delta - \frac{\omega}{2H}(P_i - P_u)\,dt\,.$$

From $d\Delta$, $e \sin \Delta$ and $e \cos \Delta$ are generated in two integrators using the sin-cos loop. Figure A.2(c):

$$d(e \cos \Delta) = -e \sin \Delta \, d\Delta$$
$$d(e \sin \Delta) = \quad e \cos \Delta \, d\Delta$$

(2) becomes

$$dP_u = i_q \, dE_Q + E_Q \, di_q .$$

This is represented as

$$-d(P_u + P_i) = -i_q \, dE_Q - E_Q \, di_q \qquad (P_i \text{ being constant}).$$

(3) becomes

$$dE_Q + de_{qm} + di_d x_{qm} = 0 .$$

These increments are accumulated in an integrator used as in Figure A.2(b). (4) becomes

$$di_q = \frac{de_{dm}}{x_{qm}} \qquad \text{where } x_{qm} \text{ is a constant.}$$

(5) has already been explained.
(6) becomes

$$d(e \sin \Delta) = e \cos \Delta \, d\Delta = de_{dm}/K_q$$

i.e. $$d(e_{dm}) = K_q e \cos \Delta \, d\Delta \qquad (K_q \text{ being a constant}).$$

(7) becomes

$$de_{qm} = dE - x_{dm} \, di_d$$

or $$-de_{qm} = x_{dm} \, di_d - dE .$$

(8) becomes

$$d(e \cos \Delta) - \frac{x_{dm} di_d}{K_d} + dE$$

or $$d(e \cos \Delta) - dE + \frac{x_{dm}}{K_d} \, di_d = 0 .$$

(9) becomes

$$\frac{E - E_{fd}}{T_{do}} \, dt = -dE + \left(1 - \frac{x'_{dm}}{x_{dm}}\right) X_{dm} \, di_d .$$

(10) becomes

$$- \frac{\mathrm{d}E_{fd}}{T_{do}} = \frac{\mu(e_m - e_r)\mathrm{d}t}{T_e T_{do}} - \frac{(E_{fd_0} - E_{fd})\mathrm{d}t}{T_e T_{do}}.$$

The integrators are linked as shown in Figures A.2(a) and A.2(b). The particular fault investigated is that which occurs when the high-voltage output terminals become earthed for a period of time. This is simulated by disconnecting the output of the integrators which generate $e \cos \varDelta$ and $e \sin \varLambda$ for the first 0·382 second thereby effectively running the alternator as if e was zero for this period of time. At the end of the fault period the correct value of e is introduced by restoring the connexions from the outputs of the $e \cos \varDelta$ and $e \sin \varLambda$ integrators and making suitable adjustments to the contents of all the integrators which are directly affected by the value of e. This is done in the following way.

At the end of the fault interval the computation is temporarily halted and the contents of those integrators which have altered are read off as whole numbers using the binary-decimal converter. From these numbers the instantaneous E_c, e_{qmc} and $\varDelta_c$ are calculated. These give new values of the following variables using equations (2)–(8),

$$0·233E = 0·155E_c + e_{qmc} - 0·922 \cos \varDelta_c$$

$$e_{qm} = 0·078E + 0·922 \cos \varDelta_c$$

$$E_Q = e_{qm} + 0·85 (E - e_{qm})$$

$$e_{dm} = 0·909 \sin \varDelta_c$$

$$i_q = 0·588 e_{dm}$$

$$P_i - P_u = 0·8 - E_Q i_q$$

$$e_m = (e_{dm}^2 + e_{qm}^2)^{\frac{1}{2}}.$$

The new contents of those integrators affected are then read in using either the card reader or directly using the decimal-binary converter.

During the fault period the output from the sin-cosine loop to the rest of the system is inhibited. This is now released when the computation is continued using the new values for E, e_{qm}, E_Q, e_{dm}, i_q, $P_i - P_u$ and e_m.

When it appears that most of the variables have reached a steady state the computation is halted and the contents of all the integrators noted, using the decimal-binary converter.

The damping constant D is given different values for different runs. However, when $\varDelta$ exceeds π the amplitude of the waves increases and a steady

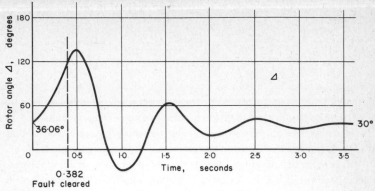

Figure A.3.

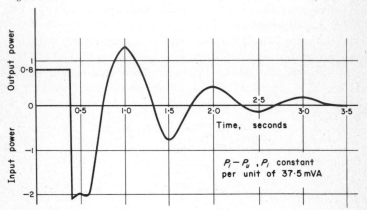

Figure A.4.

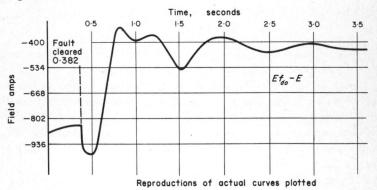

Reproductions of actual curves plotted

Figure A.5.

state is never reached. D was taken to be 1.9 sec^{-1} for the curves illustrated (Figures A.3–A.5). From these the frequency is seen to be roughly one cycle per second.

Table A.1 gives a comparison between the values of the variables of the problem, at the beginning of the fault, the end of the fault and at the end of the run, D again being 1.9 sec^{-1}.

A.4 Conclusion

With these particular equations 36 integrators including the two for driving a plotting table were used to obtain the results shown in Figures A.3, A.4, and A.5.

Since this problem was first solved a method has been evolved whereby the computer is able to put in the step function automatically at the end of the faults without any previous calculation and then continue the computation. This means that far less time is spent on each run and enables different values of D to be considered more easily in turn.

List of symbols in Appendix A

P_i prime mover input power – assumed constant.

P_u electrical output power.

H rotor inertia constant.

ω $2\pi f$

f frequency of system (50 c/s).

δ rotor angle (degrees), $\varDelta$ (radians).

t time (seconds).

E field excitation measured in terms of terminal voltage produced on open circuit, normal speed operation.

x_{dm} direct axis, synchronous rectance $\left.\right\}$ equivalent two phase

x_{qm} quadrature axis, synchronous reactance

i_d direct axis armature current $\left.\right\}$ a dual output current $= \sqrt{(i_d^2 + i_q^2)}$

i_q quadrature axis armature current

e_{dm} direct axis component of machine terminal voltage.

e_{qm} quadrature axis component of machine terminal voltage.

e_m $(e_{qm}^2 + e_{dm}^2)^{\frac{1}{2}}$

e_r reference terminal voltage

E_{fd} excitation voltage referred to armature.

T_{do} field time constant.

T_e exciter time constant.

ψ_{fd} field flux linkages.

e infinite busbar voltage (assumed to be $\frac{7}{8}$).

μ proportionality constant of voltage regulator.

x_t transformer reactance.

x_L transmission line reactance.

D damping.

x'_{dm} transient reactance.

E_Q $e_{qm} + x_{qm} i_d$

$1/K_q$ $1 + (x_T + x_L)/x_{qm}$

$1/K_d$ $1 + (x_T + X_L)/x_{dm}$

A Possible Approach to a Machine Tool Control Problem

B.1 Definition of the problem

Suppose a widely spaced set of points is given and it is required to draw a smooth curve through them. The machine will be programmed to draw a circle of continuously variable radius, the radius being varied by a servo method so that the circle will pass through the next point.

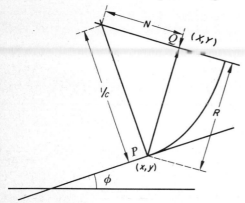

Figure B.1. *The geometry of a curve-fitting technique.*

Referring to Figure B.1, let $P(x, y)$ be the current position of the tracing point which is moving on a circle of radius of curvature c or radius $1/c$ and centre O. Let $Q(X, Y)$ be the next given point through which P will pass. Let the tangent to the curve at P make an angle ϕ with the x-axis of co-ordinates N and R being distances as defined on the diagram.

The co-ordinates of O the centre of the circle are:

$$x - r \sin \phi, \quad Y + r \sin \phi$$

where $r = 1/c$ the radius of the circle.
The distance N is then given by:

$$N^2 = (X - x + r \sin \phi)^2 + (Y - y - r \cos \phi)^2 .$$

Hence the distance with which the tracing point would miss the target point if the curvature remained constant would be $N - r$. Thus what is required is to control the radius of the circle to make $N - r$ zero and then the tracing point would pass through the target point. However, this expression is not entirely satisfactory since it takes the form $(\infty - \infty)$ when the conditions are such that the point must trace a straight line i.e. $c \neq 0$.

A more suitable criterion to take in fact is $(N^2 - r^2)/r$ which, after some reduction may be seen to be given by the following equation

$$\frac{N^2 - r^2}{r} = \frac{(X-x)^2 + (Y-y)^2}{r} + 2(X-x) - 2(Y-y) \cos \phi \, .$$

If we put $$R^2 = (X-x)^2 + (Y-y)^2$$

we obtain $$R^2 c + (2(X-x) \sin \phi - 2(Y-y) \cos \phi)$$

as the expression for the criterion.

B.2 The incremental form

If δs is the element of distance along the arc of the curve being traced then the equation for the gradient when the curvature is c is

$$\delta \phi = c \, \delta s \, .$$

The increments along the co-ordinate axes are given by:

$$x = \cos \phi \, \delta s \quad \text{and} \quad \delta y = \sin \phi \, \delta s \, .$$

The incremental relations are concerned with the computation of the error criterion e:

$$\delta(r^2) = 2(X-x) . \delta(X-x) + 2(Y-y) . \delta(Y-y) ,$$

$$\delta e = c \, \delta(r^2) + r^2 \, \delta c + 2(X-x) . \delta(\sin \phi) +$$
$$2 \sin \phi \, \delta(X-x) - 2(Y-y) \delta \cos \phi - 2 \cos \phi \, \delta(Y-y) \, .$$

The schematic of Figure B.2 is the realization of these equations.

B.3 The flow diagram

Assume the trace point moves at uniform speed along the curve, the machine time, δt, represents the increment of arc δs. δt is scaled in integrator (1). If the current curvature c is available in (2) its output is $c \, \delta s$ which is $\delta \phi$ and is put into integrators (3) and (4) to generate $\sin \phi$ and $\cos \phi$.

The outputs of (3) and (4) are also accumulated in the integrands of (6) and (7) respectively whose independent variable inputs are both δs. The outputs of (6) and (7) are then $\sin \phi \, \delta s$ and $\cos \phi \, \delta s$ respectively and are the increments of the tracing point δx and δy respectively.

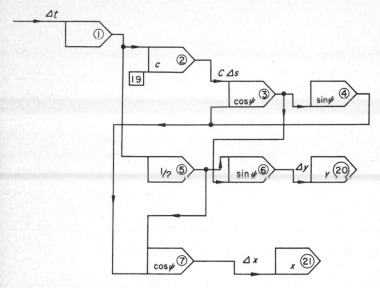

Figure B.2. *Part of the flow diagram.*

Increments δx and $-\delta x$ (defined by the target point) are summed in (8) and fed into both inputs of (10) to obtain increments of $(X - x)^2$ and similarly the output of (11) gives increments of $(Y - y)^2$. These are summed in (12) to give increments of r^2 then multiplied by c (with is assumed to be available) giving $r^2 c$. The other components of the error criterion are computed in (15), (16), (17) and (18) to give increments of $2(X - x)\sin \phi - 2(Y - y)\cos \phi$ and the increments of the criterion are accumulated in integrator (19).

This integrator which has δt as the independent variable input uses the overflow property of digital integrators and functions in the same way as a high-gain amplifier in such a way that it will put out increments until it has reduced its integrand to zero.

If this output is then connected to the various δc inputs it will perform a servo action to reduce to zero the error criterion which has accumulated in its integrand.

B.4 The results

The results of the runs are shown in Figure B.3. In the first, the co-ordinates of the target point were set when the tracing point was at $(-\frac{1}{2}, -\frac{1}{2})$ and a reasonable curve was obtained. In the second case the first target point was at

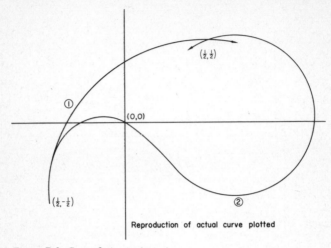

Reproduction of actual curve plotted

Figure B.3. *Curve fitting trajectories.*

$(0, 0)$ and the second target point set in when the tracing point had reached $(0, 0)$.

B.5 Conclusion

Further work needs to be done but the method seems to be promising. It is possible that some improvement could be obtained by putting in information about the next two points.

Index

197